MACROMOLECULAR STRUCTURE OF RIBONUCLEIC ACIDS

REINHOLD BOOKS IN THE BIOLOGICAL SCIENCES

CONSULTING EDITOR: PROFESSOR PETER GRAY

Department of Biological Sciences
University of Pittsburgh
Pittsburgh, Pennsylvania

The Encyclopedia of the Biological Sciences, edited by Peter Gray

Biophysics: Concepts and Mechanisms, by E. J. Casey
Cell Function, by L. L. Langley
Chordate Morphology, by Malcolm Jollie
Concepts of Forest Entomology, by Kenneth Graham
Cytology, by G. B. Wilson and John H. Morrison
Ecology of Inland Waters and Estuaries, by George K. Reid
Environmental Measurement and Interpretation, by Robert B. Platt and John F. Griffiths.
Evolution: Process and Product, Revised Edition, by Edward O. Dodson
Experimental Biology: Measurement and Analysis, by R. H. Kay
General Zoology, by Clarence J. Goodnight, Marie L. Goodnight, and Peter Gray
Introduction to Comparative Entomology, by Richard M. Fox and Jean Walker Fox
Management of Artificial Lakes and Ponds, by George W. Bennett
Manual of Insect Morphology, by E. Melville DuPorte
Natural History, by Richard A. Pimentel
Paramedical Microbiology, by Stanley E. Wedberg
The Plant Community, by Herbert C. Hanson and Ethan D. Churchill
Principles in Mammalogy, by David E. Davis and Frank B. Golley

CONSULTING EDITOR'S STATEMENT

THE PUBLICATION of this book inaugurates a new phase in Reinhold's continuing program of service to the biological sciences. This new phase is the publication of translations of outstanding books from abroad.

Professor Spirin's book is an excellent beginning for this new endeavor because the nucleic acids are in themselves exciting and there is a great dearth of translations of Russian literature in this field.

Professor Spirin's purpose in writing this book has been twofold. First to describe in clear detail the macromolecular structure of such ribonucleic acids as are known and then to see whether it is possible in the present state of our knowledge to arrive at a correlation between chemical structure and biological function. The book is excellently documented from the literature of the world and is probably the best source at present available for Soviet references in this field.

Dr. Stekol, who is responsible for editing the translation of this work, gives in his own preface a more detailed explanation of its scope.

PETER GRAY

MACROMOLECULAR STRUCTURE OF RIBONUCLEIC ACIDS

A. S. SPIRIN

A. N. Bakh Institute of Biochemistry
Academy of Sciences of USSR

Translation Editor, JACOB A. STEKOL
Head, Department of Physiological Chemistry and Nutrition
The Institute for Cancer Research
Philadelphia, Pennsylvania

New York

REINHOLD PUBLISHING CORPORATION

Chapman & Hall, Ltd., London

Library of Congress Catalog Card Number: 64-25537
Printed in The United States of America

Translated by Scripta Technica, Inc.

TRANSLATION EDITOR'S PREFACE

This book consists of two monographs by Dr. A. S. Spirin which were published approximately one year apart. They are published together in order to preserve the continuity of data and their interpretation. The earlier monograph deals mainly with the macromolecular structure of ribonucleic acids; the later one, with the relationship between the macromolecular structure of ribonucleic acids and their biological function. As one of the major contributors to the field, Dr. Spirin carefully sifts fact from theory, boldly offering new theoretical interpretations of available data as working hypotheses for further experimentation. It is hoped that the non-Russian-reading workers in this field will profit from this lucid account by Dr. Spirin of widely scattered experimental data. While visiting the Institute for Cancer Research during the Summer of 1964, Dr. Spirin carefully re-edited the Russian text of his monograph, rephrased some of the passages, deleted others, and added some clarifying notes to the text. In collaboration with Dr. Spirin, an effort was made to see to it that some Russian terms employed by him in the Russian text corresponded in meaning and usage to those common among his English-speaking colleagues. This appeared necessary because of the somewhat frivolous coinage of terms employed to describe an obscure or totally new event, particularly by the workers in the field of nucleic acids.

It is hoped that by making these monographs available in English, a small contribution will be made to the common pool of information in scientific endeavors on a worldwide scale.

J. A. Stekol
The Institute for Cancer Research,
Philadelphia, Pa.

CONTENTS

Macromolecular Structure of Ribonucleic Acids

Macromolecular Structure of Ribonucleic Acids and Biological Function

Part I

MACROMOLECULAR STRUCTURE OF RIBONUCLEIC ACIDS

Chapter I

INTRODUCTION

The critical importance of nucleic acids in the processes of growth, reproduction, heredity, virus infection, etc., is apparently determined by the major role played by these nucleic acids in the biological synthesis of proteins. The two types of nucleic acids present in every living organism—ribonucleic acid, or RNA, and deoxyribonucleic acid, or DNA—perform different functions in this key vital process. The DNA determines, with the aid of intermediary mechanisms, the specific structure of proteins synthesized in the cell, and ensures the transmission of this specificity from generation to generation. The RNA, on the other hand, participates directly in the process of biosynthesis of proteins, i.e., in the shaping of their specific structures. The central link in this process involves the complex molecular interactions of the ribosomal, "soluble" and "messenger" RNA and of "structural" proteins of ribosomes and enzymes. The concrete mechanisms of these interactions are not yet clear. For the elucidation of the molecular mechanisms underlying the functions of nucleic acids in living systems, the study of the macromolecular structure of these nucleic acids is of prime importance.

The study of physical and physiocochemical properties of RNA is, however, lagging far behind that of DNA. For many years, all attempts to isolate homogeneous polymeric RNA preparations from any biological source have failed. The isolation could not be successfully carried out because RNA proved an extremely labile compound. Relatively harsh methods, particularly those involving the use of high alkalinity, inevitably led to a rapid chemical degradation of polyribonucleotide chains. On the other hand, extraction under mild "physiological" conditions resulted, no less unavoidably, in an enzymic degradation of the nucleotides by the omnipresent ribonucleases. The matter was further complicated, for quite some time, by the lack of any effective techniques for determining the nativity, or the biologic activity, of an RNA preparation.

A high-polymeric RNA was obtained for the first time from the tobacco mosaic virus (TMV) at Stanley's laboratory (Cohen and Stanley, 1942). In this case, the very choice of the object ensured success. The purified virus contained no ribonucleases such as those present in every cell which preclude the use of mild methods. The virus RNA, isolated by a simple procedure (a virus solution was heated briefly to denature and separate the proteins) had a molecular weight up to 300,000, according to Cohen and Stanley. However, this preparation was heterogeneous, exceptionally unstable, and was rapidly degraded to chains averaging 60,000-70,000 in molecular weight. Nevertheless, the high molecular weight of the isolated virus RNA has remained a record value for many years. The best RNA preparations isolated from widely diversified cells prior to 1951 never exceeded the molecular weight range of 10,000-70,000 (Magasanik, 1955).

The first advances along this line were associated with the development of new methods for the isolation of nucleic acids. In these procedures, protein-denaturing agents were used under mild conditions with respect to pH. Volkin and Carter (1951) described a method for obtaining RNA preparations from animal tissues by using guanidine hydrochloride as a deproteinizing agent. Grinnan and Mosher (1951) also used guanidine hydrochloride for isolating high-polymeric RNA from rat liver. The RNA preparation obtained by these workers was similar to the virus RNA isolated earlier by Cohen and Stanley. It had a molecular weight of about 300,000 and was both grossly heterogeneous and unstable. The use of sodium dodecyl sulfate for the deproteinization procedure, proposed by Kay and Dounce (1953), marked a further step in the same direction. A number of subsequently developed procedures for the isolation of native RNA were based on this technique.

A remarkable solution of some technical difficulties involved in the isolation of native RNA was achieved in 1956, when phenolic deproteinization methods were proposed for the first time (Gierer and Schramm, 1956a, b; Kirby, 1956). The new procedures were based on treating the biological material with water-saturated phenol. This ensured an immediate and practically complete inactivation of the nucleases, eliminated the degradation of the RNA polyribonucleotide chains in the course of treatment, and resulted in a complete removal of proteins, thus attaining an extreme purity of the RNA preparations. Phenolic deproteinization appears to be the best of currently available methods for obtaining high-polymeric RNA from widely varied biological materials. Recently, combined use of phenol and dodecyl sulfate for RNA deproteinization has found increasing application (Shakulov et al., 1962; Hiatt, 1962; Ishihama et al., 1962; Monier et al., 1962).

Sinsheimer and co-workers were somewhat ahead of other investigators in developing improved techniques. As far back as 1954 they were able to adjust the conditions for thermal denaturation of proteins so thoroughly that they succeded in isolating from tobacco mosaic virus (TMV) an RNA with a molecular weight of about 2×10^6 (Northrop and Sinsheimer, 1954; Hopkins and Sinsheimer, 1955). As in the Cohen and Stanley experiments, an appropriate choice of the object proved to be of decisive significance, since it eliminated the need for special precautions necessary to prevent the RNA degradation by ribonuclease which might otherwise have taken place during the isolation procedure. The molecular weight of 2×10^6 was quite consistent with the total RNA content in one particle of TMV. From this it was concluded that all the RNA contained in a TMV particle exists in the form of a single molecule of a high-polymeric RNA with a molecular weight of 2×10^6. The authors were thus the first to succeed in obtaining intact undegraded (native) molecules of virus RNA.

A turning point in the investigation of high-polymeric RNA was the discovery of the intrinsic biological activity—infectivity—of the virus RNA (Gierer and Schramm, 1956a, b; Fraenkel-Conrat et al., 1957). On the basis of these studies it could now be asserted that the isolated preparations of virus RNA were in effect native, and that isolation techniques employed, especially that of phenolic deproteinization, were suitable for preserving the RNA in its native state. Needless to say, no serious inquiry into the macromolecular structure of RNA could be initiated before such a uniquely reliable criterion of nativity as the biologic activity of the preparation had been made available. Thus the discoveries made at the laboratories of Schramm and of Fraenkel-Conrat in 1956-1957 provided the much-needed point of departure in launching an effective investigation of the macrostructure of native RNA—first, the virus RNA and then the high-polymeric RNA from cellular organisms. The discovery of "soluble" RNA and the establishment of its specific biological activity (see Hoagland's review, 1960) necessitated a study of the physical properties and native structure of this type of cellular RNA.

Chapter II

LENGTH OF RNA CHAINS

1. MOLECULAR WEIGHTS

a) Virus RNA

The first investigations dating back to 1957-1958 showed that the biologically active (infectious) virus RNA from TMV is characterized (in keeping with the previously published data of Sinsheimer and co-workers) by a very high molecular weight of about 2×10^6 (Gierer, 1957, 1958a, b). One such RNA molecule constitutes the entire RNA content in one particle of TMV; in other words, one virus particle contains a single molecule of RNA. The early views advanced by Frankel-Conrat and co-workers arguing in favor of smaller molecular weights (about 300,000) of biologically active RNA from TMV (Fraenkel-Conrat et al., 1957; Fraenkel-Conrat and Singer, 1959a) were not borne out by their own experimental findings (Fraenkel-Conrat, 1959; Fraenkel-Conrat and Singer, 1959b; Haschemeyer et al., 1959). Subsequent studies, employing various methods, further confirmed that the molecular weight of native RNA from TMV is close to 2,000,000 (Ginoza, 1958, 1959; Cheo et al., 1959; Friesen and Sinsheimer,

1959; Boedtker, 1959, 1960; Spirin, Gavrilova, Bresler and Mosevitskiy, 1959). Conclusive evidence was obtained, furthermore, that no particles of virus RNA are biologically active except those whose molecular weight is no less than about 2×10^6. A single rupture in the polynucleotide chain of RNA was shown to be sufficient for its inactivation (Gierer, 1957, 1958a, b; Ginoza and Norman, 1957; Ginoza, 1958, 1959).

The isolation of infectious RNA from TMV was followed by a series of reports describing the isolation of infectious RNA from various other viruses of a ribonucleoprotein nature, beginning with the simplest viruses infecting animals and man such as viruses of the type causing poliomyelitis, diverse forms of encephalitis, foot-and-mouth disease, and also plant-infecting viruses (Schuster, 1960). In earlier experiments preceding these studies, it was shown that the absolute quantity of RNA contained in a single virus particle is the same for many of the investigated simple viruses, regardless of the size and molecular weight of the virus. This quantity is such that if all the RNA present in a single particle of a given virus is taken to consist of one molecule, then the molecular weight of the latter equals approximately 2×10^6 (Frisch-Niggemeyer, 1956). This is illustrated in Table 1. Direct molecular weight determinations of the infectious component in RNA preparations isolated from various viruses (encephalitis, foot-and-mouth disease, turnip yellow mosaic) gave a molecular weight of the order of magnitude indicated above for the infectious particle of virus RNA (Wecker, 1959; Strohmaier and Mussgay, 1959; Cheng, 1959b). Thus, besides the RNA from TMV, RNA preparations from other viruses of a ribonucleoprotein nature appear to have molecular weights close to the above, amounting to about 2×10^6. (According to

Table 1

RNA content in some viruses (according to Schuster, 1960)

Virus	Molecular weight of virus × 10^{-6}	RNA content %	Molecular weight of RNA × 10^{-6} (absolute quantity of RNA per virus particle)
Spherical plant viruses			
Turnip yellow mosaic	5	34	1.7
Tomato bushy stunt	10.65	16.5	1.65
Tobacco necrosis	8	18	1.45
Ring spottiness of tobacco ...	3.4	44	1.5
Rod-shaped plant viruses			
Tobacco mosaic	40	5.5	2.2
Potato X	37	5.5	2.0
Spherical animal infecting viruses			
Poliomyelitis............	6.7	30	2.0
Equine encephalitis	50	4.4	2.2
Myxoviruses			
Influenza (the grippe), type A .	280	0.7-1.0	≈2.0
Fowl plague	150	1.8	2.7

the most recent data, however, this is not necessarily true for all simple viruses.)

b) Ribosomal RNA

As stated earlier, the use of phenolic deproteinization for the isolation of RNA preparations from cellular organisms marks a turning point in the study of molecular weights of cellular RNA. All types of cells—of animal, plant and bacterial origin—have been shown to contain RNA having a molecular weight of the order of 10^6 (Timashev et al., 1958; Gierer, 1958c; Hall and Doty, 1958, 1959; Eisenberg and Littauer, 1958; Littauer and Eisenberg, 1958, 1959; Ts'o and Squires, 1959; Cheng, 1959a, 1960; Kurland, 1960; Osawa, 1960; Spirin and Mil'man, 1960; Spirin, 1960a; Littauer,

1961). It was further demonstrated that this high molecular weight cellular RNA constitutes a predominant fraction (80–90%) of total RNA content in cells (Hoagland, 1960). The RNA is present in cells in the form of ribonucleoprotein particles (RNP particles), or ribosomes. The acid accounts for about one half of the ribosome weight (the remaining portion is contributed by the ribosomal protein). Sedimentation studies of ribosomal RNA have shown that, in contrast to virus RNA, these acids are not monodispersed. More often than not, they consist of two discrete groups of molecules, with molecular weights, respectively, of 1,000,000–1,500,000 and about 500,000 or somewhat higher. The molecules are sufficiently monodispersed, within each group, with respect to size.

The ribosomal RNA from *E. coli*, in particular, has been studied in great detail (Littauer and Eisenberg, 1959; Littauer, 1961; Kurland, 1960; Aronson and McCarthy, 1961; Green and Hall, 1961; Spirin, 1961a; Bogdanova et al., 1962; Möller and Boedtker, 1961, 1962; Boedtker et al., 1962). It was shown to consist of two basic components, whose sedimentation coefficients are in most cases found to equal, respectively, 23 and 16–17 Svedberg units. Their respective molecular weights, according to Kurland (1960), equal 1.12×10^6 and 0.56×10^6. Intact 70 S ribosomes from *E. coli* are known to consist of two subunits, 50 S and 30 S (Tissieres and Watson, 1958; Tissieres et al., 1959). Kurland (1960) showed that each 20S subunit contains one RNA molecule whose molecular weight is 0.56×10^6 (16S RNA). Of the 50S subunits, some were found to contain one RNA molecule each, molecular weight 1.12×10^6 (23S RNA), while others contained two RNA molecules each, molecular weight 0.56×10^6 (each subunit contained two 16S RNA). These data were confirmed by Aronson and McCarthy (1961). It follows that the original 70S ribosomal particle contains, as a rule, two molecules of high-polymeric RNA—one "large" and one "small" molecule or, in some cases, three "small" molecules. Green and Hall (1961), in a special study concerned with this matter, found, however, that the 50S particles incorporated as subunits into 70S ribosomes ("derivative" 50S particles) each contain one large RNA component (23S) in nearly every case. The so-called native 50S particles, on the other hand, i.e., particles that exist independently in the cell and not as subunits of 70S ribosomes, were each shown to contain two small RNA molecules (16S). Hence, the two-component structure of ribosomal RNA from *E. coli* indicates that ribosomal particles of the basic type (70S) consist of two unequal subunits, 50S and 30S, each containing a single RNA molecule (23S and 16S, respectively). This appears to be a common property of all ribosomal RNA, including those isolated from other organisms and cells.

Unfortunately, up to now, complete and reliable comparative studies on molecular weights of ribosomal RNA from various multicellular organisms have been rather limited in number. Comparison of data on molecular weights reported by different authors is not likely to prove of much help, considering that the experimental conditions, the quality of preparations and the methods of calculation differed widely in each case.

For the components of ribosomal RNA preparations obtained from various animal and plant cells (rat liver, tobacco leaves, brain tissue of mice, calf's thymus nuclei), Gierer (1958c) and Cheng (1959a, 1960) reported respective molecular weights ranging 1.7-1.8×10^6 and about 0.6-0.7×10^6 (the molecular weight ratio equaling 3:1-2.5:1). The sedimentation coefficients of the RNA components, according to their data, amounted to about 30 and 17-18 Svedberg units. Comparable sedimentation coefficients equaling 32-34 and 15-18 Svedberg units, respectively, were recorded by Timashev et al. (1958) and Kronman et al. (1960) for RNA from cells of Ehrlich's ascites cancer. Molecular weights of 2.3×10^6 and 3.2×10^5 were calculated for the respective RNA components. Sedimentation coefficients of 28 and 18 Svedberg units, respectively, were obtained by Hall and Doty (1959) for RNA from microsomes of calf's liver, and by Ts'o and Squires (1959) for RNA from microsomes from peas and from reticulocytes of the rabbit. Calculations of molecular weights, according to Hall and Doty, yielded values of 1.3×10^6 and 0.6×10^6. Sedimentation coefficients of 28 and 17 Svedberg units, for ribosomal RNA from calf's liver, were cited also by Littauer (1961). For high molecular weight RNA from rat liver, respective values of 17-18 and 25-26 Svedberg units were reported by Laskov et al. (1959) and Littauer (1961). The sedimentation coefficients of the two RNA components were still less at variance in the case of RNA from chick's liver, amounting to 24 and 19 Svedberg units (Littauer, 1961). In our experiments (Spirin, 1961a), sedimentation coefficients of 24.5 and 14.5 Svedberg units were obtained for RNA from bone marrow of rabbit, and 25.1 and 13.9 Svedberg units for RNA from pea seedlings. Molecular weight calculations gave values of 1.27×10^6 and 0.53×10^6 for the RNA obtained from rabbit (ratio $M_1 : M_2 = 3:1$), and 1.34×10^6 and 0.39×10^6 for the RNA obtained from peas (ratio $M_1 : M_2 = 3.5:1$).

If we pause to consider discrepancies between sedimentation coefficients as determined by various authors, employing the same materials, two possible basic causes will suggest themselves. First, sedimentation at low temperature, with subsequent reduction of data to standard conditions (20° C), will yield somewhat higher values for $S_{20,w}$ as compared with sedimentation carried out at room temperature, owing to the more compact state of the RNA macromolecule at a low temperature level. Second, the possible presence of magnesium ions and other bivalent cations in RNA preparations will likewise lead to elevated sedimentation coefficients for RNA components, because of the greater compactness of RNA particles under these conditions. Differences in procedure appear to be responsible, to cite one instance, for lower $S_{20,w}$ values obtained in our experiments for RNA from peas and rabbits (Spirin, 1961a) as compared with data reported by Ts'o and Squires (1960). In our tests, the RNA was reprecipitated from a "Versene" solution before sedimentation, and the latter was carried out in the presence of "Versene" at 20° C. The effect of magnesium and reduced temperature, resulting in higher RNA sedimentation coefficients, was clearly demonstrated by Boedtker (1959, 1960) and by Möller and Boedtker (1962). For instance, the RNA from *E. coli*, whose components usually have sedimentation coefficients of 23 and 16 Svedberg units, sediment, in the presence of magnesium, at the rates of 29 and 21 Svedberg units, respectively (Möller and Boedtker, 1962). The very high sedimentation coefficients, particularly those for the large component, obtained by Timashev et al. (1958), Kronman et al. (1960), Gierer (1958c) and Cheng (1959a, 1960) can presumably be best explained by the presence of bivalent cations in the preparations and, in experiments of Gierer, by the low temperatures employed. The molecular weights calculated by these authors for the large component may have been somewhat high. In that case, we are dealing with a component of a large ribosomal subunit similar to the one in *E. coli* (23S RNA), rather than with a single RNA molecule contained in an intact ribosomal particle.

The variability of sedimentation coefficients, as shown above, calls for extreme caution in comparing data cited by different authors. This applies especially to any attempt at using molecular weight/sedimentation coefficient ratios, derived for one set of experimental conditions, to calculate molecular weights of other preparations obtained under different conditions or by different authors. Highly indicative comparison data can therefore be obtained only in experiments carried out at the same laboratory, with RNA freed of bivalent cations in order to obviate chance variations of their content in the preparations.

Table 2 summarizes data on various high-polymeric RNA obtained in our laboratory under identical conditions. Measurements were performed in the presence of 0.01 M "Versene," the ionic strength equaling 0.1. All molecular weights were calculated by the use of an empirical equation derived for specified experimental conditions: $M = 1550 \times S^{2.1}$ (Spirin, 1961a).

Table 2

Sedimentation coefficient and molecular weights of high-polymeric RNA's (according to Spirin, 1961a)

Source of RNA	$S^0_{20,w}$	$M \times 10^{-6}$ (M_1, M_2)	Sum of $M \times 10^{-6}$ ($M_1 + M_2$)
TMV	31.0	2.1	2.1
E. coli	23.0 16.7	1.12 0.56	1.7
Rabbit	24.5 14.5	1.27 0.43	1.7
Peas	25.1 13.9	1.34 0.39	1.7

From the tabulated data, it can be concluded that, apparently, molecular weight values for ribosomal RNA are not uniform but may vary slightly depending on the biological source involved.

Characteristically, the values of $S_{20,w}$ for the small component decrease with higher $S_{20,w}$ values for the large component, as shown by comparison of sedimentation coefficients for RNA isolated from different organisims. This is further confirmed by the data of Littauer (1961) on ribosomal RNA obtained from different animal species:

Chick. . . . . 24 and 19 Svedberg units
Rat . . . . . . 26 and 18 Svedberg units
Calf. . . . . . 28 and 17 Svedberg units

This apparently indicates that the higher molecular weight of the large component of ribosomal RNA of a given organism is accompanied by a lower molecular weight of a small component of the RNA, that is, an increase in the molecular weight of one component is accompanied by a decrease in the molecular weight of the other. The cited data (Spirin, 1961a; Littauer, 1961) suggest that the molecular weight ratio, for the two basic components of ribosomal RNA, may vary for different organisms. The 2:1 ratio obtained for ribosomes from *E. coli* will not necessarily hold for ribosomes isolated from other cells and organisms. Our data (Spirin, 1961a) show a ratio of about 3:1 for ribosomal RNA from rabbit and peas. This value is at variance with the earlier data of Ts'o (1958), who cited a molecular weight ratio of 2:1 for the subunits of pea ribosomes.

The most interesting conclusion that can be arrived at after considering the data in Table 2 is that the sum of molecular weights for the large and the small component in ribosomal RNA appears to be the same in all cases, irrespective of the type of cell—bacterial, plant or animal. This sum equals 1.7×10^6, which is close to the molecular weight of virus RNA. It follows that each intact

(70S or 80S) ribosome particle, which as a rule contains a single molecule of the large component in ribosomal RNA and a single molecule of the small component, has invariably the same RNA content, irrespective of the source organism, and that the RNA content in one such ribosome is close to that in one virus particle.

Exactly the same conclusion was reached much earlier on the basis of a direct comparison of RNA content in various ribosomes and viruses (Cheng, 1957; Tissieres and Watson, 1958). The 70S ribosome in *E. coli* is known to have a molecular weight of 2.8×10^6 and to contain 60–65% RNA, that is, the molecular weight calculated for the total RNA content amounts to 1.7×10^6. The 80S yeast ribosome has a molecular weight of 4.1×10^6 and contains 42% RNA; this gives again the value of 1.7×10^6 for total RNA content. A molecular weight of $4.0–4.5 \times 10^6$ and RNA content amounting to 40% were obtained for the 80S particle of pea seedlings, giving a value of 1.7×10^6 for the molecular weight of RNA.

The significance of the indicated universality is not yet clear. The possibility must be reckoned with that any high molecular weight RNA particle at some particular stage of formation or function in the cell, may exist as a single molecule with a molecular weight of about 2×10^6.

It can be assumed, for one thing, that the cellular mechanisms of the synthesis of high-polymeric RNA are so organized that they normally produce polyribonucleotides with molecular weights close to 2×10^6. It is possible that such a mechanism reproduces the precursors of ribosomal RNA with molecular weights approximating 2×10^6, and which prior to, in the course of, or after their formation become split into two unequal fractions. This would account for the fact that the total RNA content in a normal ribosome always corresponds to a molecular weight of about 2×10^6.

c) "Soluble" RNA

Another fraction of cellular RNA, which accounts for 10-20% of the total RNA content in the cell, is the so-called soluble RNA (adaptor RNA), sometimes referred to as "transfer" RNA or "acceptor" RNA. The molecular weight of this RNA is nearly two orders lower than that of high-polymeric RNA. According to the most reliable physicochemical measurements (Tissieres, 1959; Brown and Zubay, 1960; Cox and Littauer, 1960), it equals about 25,000-30,000, which corresponds to not more than 80-100 nucleotides. In all active molecules of "soluble" RNA, the end nucleotides are arranged in a characteristic sequence: C-C-A. The nativity of preparations which belong to this class of cellular RNA is easily established by testing their specific biological ability. The latter can be defined as the ability to combine with activated amino acids and transfer these to the ribosomes, in the presence of appropriate enzyme systems (see Hoagland's review, 1960).

d) "Messenger" RNA

The most important fraction of intracellular RNA, the study of which began only recently, is information RNA, known also as intermediary RNA (m-RNA). This fraction of intracellular RNA is generally found in cells in relatively small amounts (apparently not exceeding 5-8% of total RNA content). It is possible that m-RNA molecules vary in size, corresponding to the size variation in proteins synthesized in the cells. Early determinations showed a molecular weight of about 100,000 as the most likely value for the bulk of bacterial m-RNA molecules. (The sedimentation coefficient, after deproteinization, equals about 8 Svedberg units: Nomura et al., 1960; Gros et al., 1961a, b.) In recent research, however, the previously reported values of sedimentation coefficients and molecular weights were shown to have been obtained under conditions of a partial enzymic degradation of the original (native) m-RNA molecules, which took place during the process of cell destruction and subsequent isolation of the RNA preparation. Recent experiments described by many authors lead to the conclusion that in the case of m-RNA, molecular weights vary over a wide range from 20,000-50,000 to 2×10^6 and higher. The sedimentation coefficients vary from 4 to 30 Svedberg units in *E. coli* and may be as high as 45 Svedberg units in animal cells (Spiegelman, 1961; Takai et al., 1962; Scherer and Darnell, 1962; Hiatt, 1962; Ishihama et al., 1962; Monier et al., 1962). The relative fraction of high molecular components in m-RNA is found to be quite large.

2. "TEMPERATURE EFFECT" AND CONTINUITY OF POLYNUCLEOTIDE CHAINS

a) Virus RNA

Historically it so happened that biological acitivity as the basis for the native state of the isolated preparations was first demonstrated for the virus RNA. This cleared the way at once for exploring the macromolecular structure of native RNA.

As mentioned earlier, soon after biologically active (infectious) RNA had been isolated from TMV, a heated controversy developed. One group maintained that the infectious unit is a continuous polynucleotide chain having a molecular weight of 2,000,000. The other group, headed by Fraenkel-Conrat, maintained at first that the RNA contained in a virus particle consisted of separate molecules, or subunits (molecular weight, about 300,000), and that these were the only biologically active units (see Chapter II, 1a). Time soon settled the issue in favor of the first view. It has been shown, and confirmed, in a long series of observations that the biologically active molecule of virus RNA, whose molecular weight equals about 2×10^6, consists of a single continuous nucelotide chain made up of 6000–7000 nucleotide residues (Gierer, 1957, 1958a, b; Ginoza, 1958, 1959; Spirin, Gavrilova, Bresler, Mosevitskiy, 1959; Fraenkel-Conrat et al., 1962; Fraenkel-Conrat and Singer, 1959b).

The effect of heating on viscosimetric and sedimentational properties of virus RNA was tested by the authors in collaboration with L. P. Gavrilova, at the laboratory headed by A. N. Belozerskii. The experiments had a decisive influence on further studies of continuity versus discontinuity of the polynucleotide chains in RNA. In early 1959 the study led to the discovery of a new behavioral phenomenon displayed by high-polymeric RNA, which we named the "temperature effect" (Gavrilova, Spirin and Belozersky, 1959). The detection of this phenomenon followed by the elucidation of its nature, provided some clues to the solution of many other questions regarding the macromolecular structure of RNA. The effect first became apparent during heating for a definite time as an abrupt steep rise of specific viscosity of native virus RNA, accompanied by a simultaneous decline of the sedimentation coefficient.

Cited below is a description of the first experiments designed to test the effect of heating on virus RNA in solution and, further, to disclose the operating mechanism involved (Gavrilova et al., 1959). In these early tests, unlike the subsequent ones, relatively high RNA concentrations were used. Much the same regularity patterns were observed in further experiments with RNA in low concentrations. No differences were noted, except in the absolute values obtained for a number of indices (Spirin, Gavrilova et al., 1959b).

In these tests, we used solutions of virus RNA in a phosphate buffer, pH 7.2, ionic strength 0.1, as well as in a 6 *M* urea solution buffered with phosphate to the same pH value and ionic strength as indicated above. (A check on the infectivity of these solutions showed that urea does not inactivate virus RNA.) The character of temperature dependence of reduced viscosity of solutions of infectious RNA is illustrated in Fig. 1. It is seen from curve 1 that a temperature rise from 20 to 40°C produced no change in reduced viscosity. Further increase of temperature caused a sharp rise in viscosity, reaching a peak value at 60 to 70°C. A transition of RNA molecules from one state to another is thus seen to have taken place within a rigorously defined and rather narrow temperature interval. This transition, in contrast to thermal denaturing of proteins, caused no immediate inactivation of macromolecules (in this, to a loss of infectivity). The process was therefore a reversible one.

It should be pointed out that no temperature effect was noted in the case of RNA preparations which had lost their infectivity, i.e., no rise in viscosity was noted within the 40-60°C interval, although at 20°C their viscosimetric indices may have been the same as those of infectious preparations (Fig. 1, curve 2). The rise in viscosity on heating was found to vary linearly with the infectious activity of a given RNA preparation.

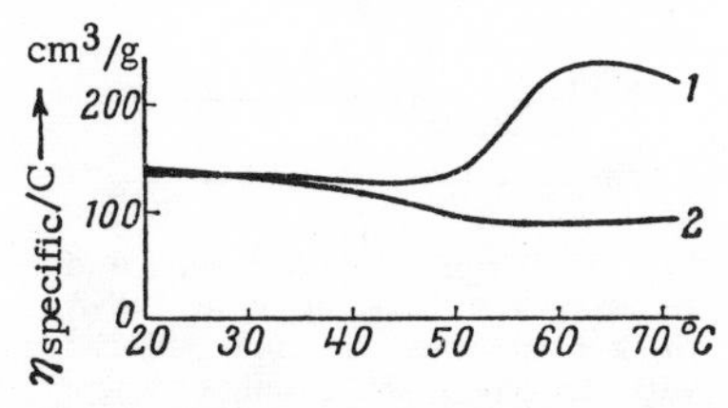

Fig. 1. Temperature dependence of reduced viscosity of virus RNA in phosphate buffer, pH 7, ionic strength 0.1. 1—Infectious RNA; 2—RNA infectivity lost after standing of solution (Gavrilova et al., 1959).

An even more pronounced temperature effect on infectious RNA was observed in a study of the dependence of reduced viscosity on temperature, employing RNA in a 6 *M* urea solution buffered with phosphate to an ionic strength of 0.1 (pH 7.2). The results are shown in Fig. 2 (curve 1). The transition temperature for infectious RNA changing to a state of high viscosity is seen to have been considerably reduced in the presence of 6 *M* urea. The transition was accomplished largely within the 30-50° C interval. The extent of rise in viscosity for freshly prepared infectious RNA was considerably greater than in the case of a phosphate-buffered solution. On heating the 6 *M* urea solution (ionic strength = 0.1) to 50°C both the specific and reduced viscosities of infectious RNA increased more than fourfold. As in the case of the heated phosphate-buffered solution, the change in viscosity with temperature was reversible and was not associated with inactivation of the RNA.

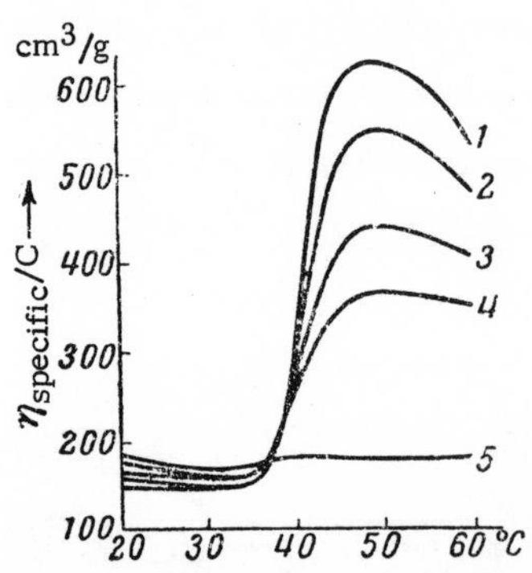

Fig. 2. Temperature dependence of reduced viscosity of virus RNA in a 6 *M* urea solution buffered with phosphate, pH 7, ionic strength 0.1.
1—Infectious RNA on the day of preparation; 2, 3, 4—same RNA solution with diminished infectivity; 5—RNA infectivity completely lost (Gavrilova et al., 1959).

The extent of rise in viscosity, on heating to 50° C, was again found to be a function of the infectious activity of RNA preparations (Fig. 2, curves 2-4). Complete loss of infectivity eliminated the temperature effect (Fig. 2, curve 5).

The sedimentation of virus RNA at various temperatures was studied next in an attempt to establish the nature of the temperature effect observed in experiments with infectious RNA and, in addition, to trace the causes of its absence in the case of noninfectious preparations. In the presence of urea, temperatures at which higher viscosities were noted were shifted toward a lower level. This made it possible to attain an equal, or greater, increase in specific viscosity at lower temperatures of the RNA solution. For this reason, RNA sedimentation under heating was carried out in 6 *M* urea solutions with phosphate buffer, pH 7.2, at ionic strength of 0.1. Sedimentation diagrams are reproduced in Figs. 3 and 4.

Sedimentation at 55-50° C in a 6 *M* urea solution buffered with phosphate showed a very sharp peak in the photo obtained for infectious RNA at this temperature (see Fig. 4). The sedimentation coefficient, however, when reduced to standard conditions (water, 20° C), fell to about one-third of the value obtained at 20° C (compare lines 5 and 6 in Table 3).

Thus, heating an infectious RNA solution to 50° C in the presence of urea caused a more than threefold increase in specific viscosity, accompanied by a drop in the sedimentation coefficient to one-third its value. This indicates that the observed temperature effect is associated with a sharp increase in the asymmetry or the molecular volume of the RNA particles. It was concluded that heating causes a complete or partial unfolding of the polynucleotide chain in RNA, while at lower temperatures this

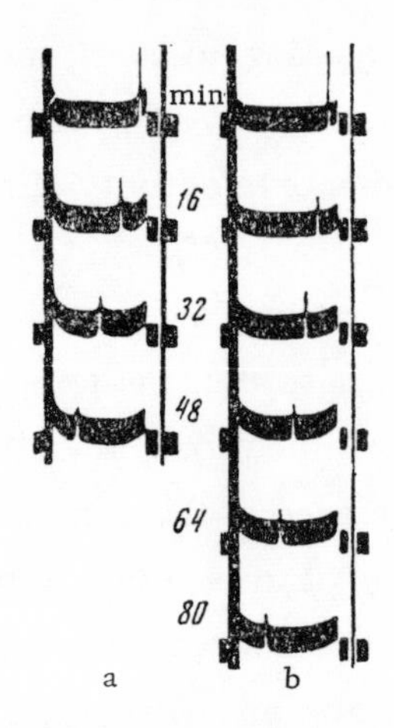

Fig. 3. Sedimentation of infectious virus RNA preparation at 20°C, 50,740 rpm, photographed at 16-minute intervals. From top to bottom:
a—In a phosphate buffer, pH 7, ionic strength 0.1; b—in a 6 *M* urea solution buffered with phosphate, pH 7, ionic strength 0.1 (Gavrilova et al., 1959).

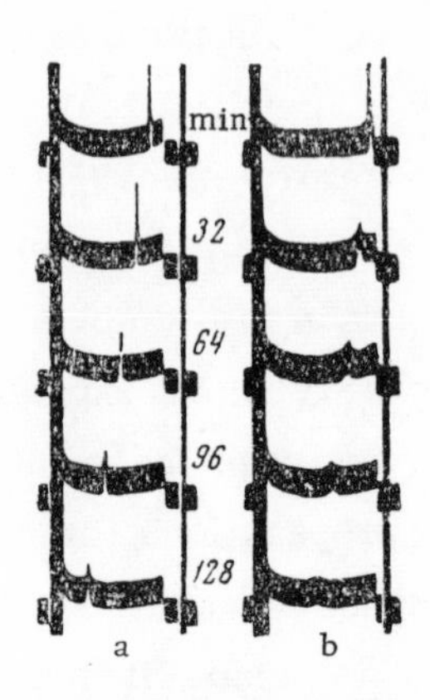

Fig. 4. Sedimentation of RNA preparation at 55–50°C in 6 *M* urea and phosphate, pH 7, ionic strength 0.1, before and after loss of infectivity; 50,740 rpm; photographed at 32-minute intervals. From top to bottom:
a—Infectious RNA; b—the same RNA after loss of infectivity (Gavrilova et al., 1959).

chain is folded into a compact particle of a certain shape. The fact that urea lowers the transition temperatures at which the macromolecules pass into an unfolded state strongly indicates the rupture of hydrogen bonds as a major factor responsible for the temperature effect as described above.

In Fig. 4 (right-hand side) a single peak is shown again, though not nearly as sharp, and much wider, for the sedimentation of an RNA preparation which had lost its infectivity, in a 6 *M* urea solution buffered with phosphate at 55-60° C. The sedimentation coefficient, however, was close to that obtained for infectious RNA and for the same temperature (see Table 3, line 8). At 50° C, therefore, the noninfectious preparation will show a considerably lower viscosity but about the same sedimentation

Table 3

Sedimentation coefficients* and viscosity of RNA preparations at different temperatures (according to Gavrilova et al., 1959)

Solvent	RNA, mg/ml	Infectivity	°C	$\eta_{specific}/C$ cm^3/g	$S_{20,\,w}$ Svedberg units
Phosphate buffer, pH 7, ionic strength 0.1	4.4	Infectious	20 70	136 230	16.0 -
		Noninfectious	20 70	138 90	16 -
6 *M* urea and phosphate, pH 7, ionic strength 0.1	3.6	Infectious	20 52.5	160 520	14.6** 4.8**
		Noninfectious	20 52.5	180 180	16-23 4.6

*Sedimentation coefficients reduced to standard conditions (water, 20°C).
**Respective sedimentation coefficients for infectious virus RNA in 6 *M* urea and phosphate, at infinitie dilution, equal 30 Svedberg units at 20°C and 10.5 Svedberg units at 55-50°C (in both cases, the values are reduced to standard conditions: water, 20°C) (Spirin, Gavrilova, Bresler and Mosevitskiy, 1959).

coefficient as noninfectious RNA. In the light of this evidence we feel justified in assuming that at 50° C the molecules of infectious RNA, in a 6 *M* urea solution (ionic strength, 0.1), exist as more or less unfolded single-stranded chains in contrast to RNA that has lost its infectivity, which consists of much shorter chains.

No distinct difference in particle size between infectious and noninfectious RNA can be discerned, however, from sedimentation and viscosity data obtained at 20° C (see Table 3, lines 1 and 3, 5 and 7). It was in fact shown in an earlier report from this laboratory that in the process of spontaneous loss of infectivity, the molecules of virus RNA (from TMV) may not break up at once into finer subunits and may thus retain their original high mean molecular weight while in solutions at room temperature (Gavrilova and Spirin, 1959). From these data it was concluded that in spontaneous loss of infectivity, the continuous single-strand structure of native RNA passes over into a discontinuous one, even though to all appearances the macromolecule, as an integral entity, may remain intact. The particle, in this case, will appear to be built of "subunits," which will easily "dissociate" in a heated solution (Gavrilova et al., 1959). This was confirmed in recent tests on RNA from the turnip yellow mosaic virus (Haselkorn, 1962). A clear distinction between the continuous (native) polynucleotide chain of virus RNA and the discontinuous (damaged) chain becomes apparent on heating the RNA solution to appropriate temperature, at which the continuous chains (in infectious molecules) will be unfolded. This will result in a marked thickening of the solution, which will be reflected in an abrupt rise of specific viscosity. The shorter chains of noninfectious RNA, on the other hand, will become dissociated, causing no increase in specific viscosity (Gavrilova et al., 1959).*

Thus, the presence and magnitude of a temperature effect (rise of specific viscosity on heating) proved to be a reliable physicochemical criterion of the infectivity of virus RNA preparations. This rise, on the other hand, is directly associated with the continuity of the polynucleotide chains in native virus RNA. Consequently, a severalfold increase in specific viscosity on heating could be employed as a general test for the continuity of polynucleotide chains in any RNA molecules under consideration. Such a testing technique was, in fact, widely used in our further

---

*When a virus RNA preparation which has lost its infectivity is heated, its specific viscosity may either remain unchanged or show a slight decline. This will depend on the extent of "latent degradation" of the polynucleotide chain. The decline in specific viscosity on heating will be the more pronounced as the number of ruptures in the chain increases. If there are but a few ruptures, viscosity may remain fairly constant (or become slightly higher). In the latter case, the diminution of viscosity caused by the dissociation of particles, due to heating, is counterbalanced by a thermal unfolding of the fragments, which tends to thicken the solution (i.e., to increase its specific viscosity).

experiments with various RNA's, and with ribosomes (Spirin, 1961a, 1962a; Bogdanova et al., 1962; Shakulov et al., 1962).

b) Ribosomal RNA

While it is now generally recognized that the molecule of infectious virus RNA consists of a single continuous polynucleotide chain of 2,000,000 molecular weight, no such agreement, until recently, has been reached with respect to ribosomal RNA.

At Doty's laboratory it was shown for the first time that the molecules of ribosomal RNA dissociate when the solution is heated. This was due to a thermal rupture of hydrogen bonds which hold together the individual subunits of RNA (Hall and Doty, 1958, 1959). The molecular weight of subunits was found to equal about 100,000. Within a short time, the concept which pictures the ribosomal RNA particle as made up of individual subunits won nearly general recognition (see, for example, Hoagland's review, 1960). Experimental evidence in support of this theory has been obtained in many other laboratories which have shown that each molecule of ribosomal RNA consists not of one continuous chain but of shorter chains (subunits) varying in number. After Hall and Doty, other authors (Takanami, 1960; Osawa, 1960; Tashiro et al., 1960; Aronson and McCarthy, 1961; Helmkamp and Ts'o, 1961) observed the formation of particles with a lower molecular weight, in solutions of various ribosomal RNA's subjected to heating. This was explained as due to the presence of subunits in the macromolecule of ribosomal RNA, held together by "weak" bonds, which became ruptured on heating. It was assumed that such "weak" bonds could be provided either by hydrogen bonds or by bridges made up of bivalent or multivalent metals. To verify the latter assumption, Aronson and McCarthy (1961) dialyzed a solution of ribosomal RNA from *E. coli* against a buffer containing no magnesium. As a result, these authors were able to observe an actual disintegration of the RNA molecule into fragments with molecular weights of down to 30,000. Brown et al. (1960) noted a reversible dissociation of the animal ribosomal RNA into subunits on addition of an approximately equal amount of protein (bovine serum albumin, bovine γ-globulin, or α-lactoalbumin). According to recent reports (Helmkamp and Ts'o, 1961; Ts'o and Helmkamp, 1961), ribosomal RNA from pea seedlings, consisting originally of two components with, respectively, sedimentation coefficients of 27-28 and 17-18 Svedberg units, undergoes an irreversible dissociation into subunits due to a rupture of the hydrogen bonds. This effect is achieved with the aid of formamide or dimethyl sulfoxide, as well as by heating the aqueous solution. Following such treatment, the acid, brought back into solution at room temperature, undergoes sedimentation as a heterogeneous peak, with a mean sedimentation coefficient of 8-10 Svedberg units. It was further noted by these authors that virus RNA, when dissolved in formamide, shows no change in molecular weight or infectivity (Ts'o et al., 1960). Again the obvious conclusion—or so it seemed—was that ribosomal RNA, unlike virus RNA, consists of subunits held together by hydrogen bonds, rather than of continuous chains.

A different concept was proposed in our reports (Spirin and Mil'man, 1960; Spirin, 1960, 1961a) concerning the structure of ribosomal RNA. The validity of data obtained by Hall and Doty, as well as of ample experimental evidence confirming their results, was questioned for the first time, since our own experiments showed no chain dissociation in ribosomal RNA following heat treatment.

In our first attempt to check directly the results reported by Hall and Doty, we used high-polymeric RNA from animal tissues. In isolating this acid, we eliminated the preliminary step of obtaining a microsome preparation. Instead, a direct phenolic deproteinization of tissue was applied, followed by the separation of high-polymeric (ribosomal) RNA by precipitation with 1.5 M NaCl solution. The RNA was isolated from such material as rat liver, cells of ascites rat hepatoma, and rabbit bone marrow (Spirin and Mil'man, 1960; Spirin, 1961a). Characteristic temperature dependence of reduced viscosity on temperature of high-polymeric animal RNA is shown in Figs. 5 and 6. The data show the same abrupt steep rise in viscosity in a heated solution of high-polymeric animal RNA as was previously observed for virus RNA. It is of interest that on letting the RNA solution stand the extent of rise in specific viscosity decreases or is totally absent, as is the case with virus RNA which undergoes spontaneous inactivation if the solution is left to stand.

These findings are at variance with the data of Hall and Doty regarding decrease in specific viscosity of RNA in heated solutions. In our experiments no such decrease was noted, except in RNA preparations left standing in solution for a long time and therefore subjected to a spontaneous degradation. We concluded that Hall and Doty must have experimented with high-polymeric RNA whose primary structure had been damaged to begin with. Native preparations of high-polymeric RNA from animal tissues apparently do not dissociate into subunits on heating, since each particle consists of a single continuous polynucleotide chain, as is the case with virus RNA.

Our experimental work with high-polymeric RNA designed to test the effect of heating on the state of the macromolecules was

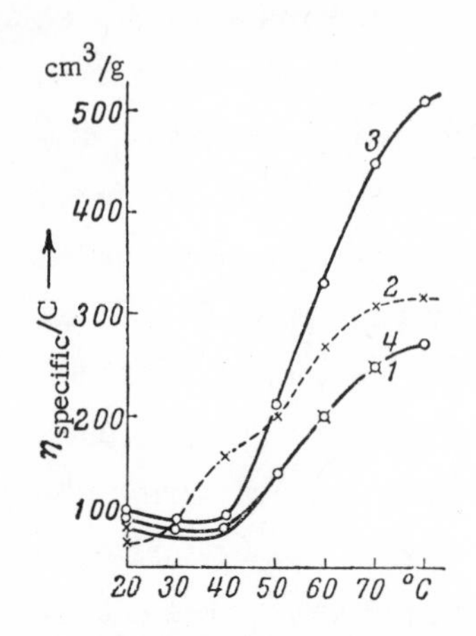

Fig. 5. Temperature dependence of viscosity of high-polymeric rat RNA. 1—RNA from rat liver in a phosphate buffer, pH 7.2, ionic strength 0.1, RNA concentration 3 mg/ml; 2—RNA from rat liver in a 6 *M* urea solution buffered with phosphate, pH 7.2, ionic strength 0.1, RNA concentration 3 mg/ml; 3, 4—two different RNA preparations from ascites hepatoma in rats, phosphate buffer, pH 7.2, ionic strength 0.1, RNA concentration 3 mg/ml (for 3) and 2 mg/ml (for 4); curve 4 coincides with curve 1. (Spirin and Mil'man, 1960).

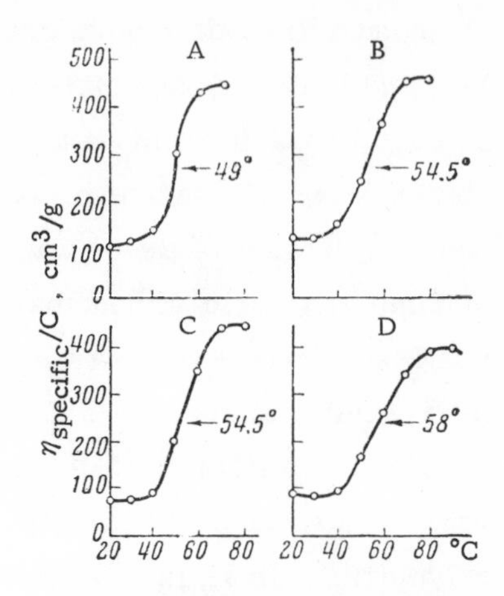

Fig. 6. Temperature dependence of viscosity of high-polymeric RNA preparation from various sources. Solvent—phosphate buffer, ionic strength 0.1, plus "Versene" to 0.01 concentration, pH 7.3.
A—RNA from TMV, 1.6 mg/ml; B—RNA from pea seedlings, 2.5 mg/ml; C—RNA from *E. coli*, 2.3 mg/ml; D—RNA from bone marrow of rabbit, 2.5 mg/ml (Spirin, 1961).

extended to other ribosomal RNA's—among these, bacterial RNA obtained either from the protoplasts of *E. coli* or from the isolated ribosomes of this organism, as well as plant RNA isolated from pea seedlings (Spirin, 1961a; Bogdanova et al., 1962). The respective curves, showing temperature dependence of viscosity, are given in Fig. 6 (C) and (B). The graph shows the same type of "temperature effect" as seen before, namely, an abrupt rise in specific viscosity on heating, which indicates the presence of continuous polynucleotide chains in the high-polymeric RNA under investigation. Sedimentation experiments carried out at elevated temperatures, on preparations of high-polymeric (ribosomal) RNA from *E. coli*, demonstrated that in this case, as in the case of virus RNA, the sedimentation rate is reduced (by about two-thirds) with an increase in viscosity. The latter, therefore, reflects a thermal uncoiling of continuous polynucleotide chains, as seen in earlier experiments (Bogdanova et al., 1962).

A manifold increase in specific viscosity, caused by the thermal unfolding of polynucleotide chains, as in the case of virus RNA, was demonstrated for all the tested ribosomal RNA (Fig. 6). A point to be stressed is that such viscosity changes with temperature were found to be reversible, as shown previously for infectious virus RNA. When the heated solution had cooled to its original temperature, the viscosity regained its original value. The sedimentation pattern, too, was completely restored on cooling of the solution, and the same two components were in evidence at 20° C, along with their previous sedimentation coefficients. "Versene," even when present in relatively large concentration, had no effect whatever on the magnitude or reversibility of the rise in viscosity, as compared with experiments carried out in a phosphate buffer without "Versene." A considerable rise in specific viscosity noted for high-polymeric RNA following heat treatment is not consistent with the presumed dissociation of macromolecules. More likely, it reflects uncoiling of sufficiently long chains, such as those previously displayed by infectious virus RNA. The reversibility of viscosity changes makes it evident that neither the unfolding of chains nor the rupture of hydrogen bonds on heating causes any dissociation of the original macromolecules, nor do these macromolecules disintegrate into separate chains of shorter length, or "subunits."

It follows that all the high-polymeric RNA's tested in the above experiments behaved as long, continuous polynucleotide chains undergoing thermal uncoiling.

It can be argued that in these tests the brief heating period was not sufficient to cause dissociation of some unknown noncovalent bonds which held together the "subunits." The argument lacks substantiation, however. The noncovalent bonds in question are supposed to link more or less firmly the "subunits" contained within a single macromolecule. Only hydrogen bonds can achieve such linkage, through their nitrogenous bases or some complex metallic bonds. There is no immediate dissociation in high-polymeric RNA even when heated to 80-90° C (the temperature at which the hydrogen bonds, whose concerted action holds together polynucleotide chains of sufficient length, of the type present in DNA, become ruptured). In polymeric RNA, furthermore, a maximum hyperchromic effect is attained at the unfolding temperature (see below), i.e., at a time when no appreciable number of hydrogen bonds could remain intact.

In the light of these observations, it seems most unlikely that separate subunits could actually be held together by hydrogen bonds to form a single macromolecule. Nor will the second assumption—that of metallic bonds acting in the same capacity—appear any more plausible if we consider that "Versene," even when present in comparatively large concentrations, has no effect on viscosity, sedimentation rate, or molecular weight values found for RNA at room temperature. Even more indicative is the fact that "Versene" influences neither the increase in viscosity due to heating nor the reversibility of any of the indices.

The point is that it seems much easier to obtain an apparent "dissociation" of molecules in ribosomal RNA than not to obtain it. Such a false picture of "dissociation" is possible because an RNA polynucleotide chain is highly vulnerable. Of particular importance are the following possibilities regarding such artifacts: (a) thermal degradation of the polynucleotide chain, especially where prolonged heating is applied; (b) enzymic degradation, effected largely by traces of ribonucleases, found invariably in any RNA preparation; (c) the case where a few pre-existing ruptures in the polynucleotide chain are in evidence, which occurred in the course of the ribosome isolation. Such ruptures are not detectable at room temperature, because the integrity of the compact particle is sustained by the hydrogen bonds. Should the latter become ruptured, a dissociation of the particle into separate constituent chains will follow, in effect. This was shown for numerous preparations of virus RNA which had lost its infectivity (see above: II, 2, a; Gavrilova et al., 1959; Haselkorn, 1962). It has recently been demonstrated at our laboratory (Shakulov et al., 1962) that the intactness (continuity) of an RNA polynucleotide chain may be disrupted, while still in the ribosome, without any apparent change in the physicochemical properties of the latter. Such impairment (latent degradation of ribosomal RNA inside the ribosome) may occur "spontaneously" in the process of obtaining a ribosome preparation. It can also be effected deliberately by exposing the ribosome particle to the action of the exogenous ribonuclease in low concentrations. The treatment will not affect the sedimentation characteristics of the particle.

Now, what happens if the experimenter does not insist on obtaining a continuous chain at all costs, but takes the opposite approach? In that case, a degradation or evidence of a pre-existing impairment of the polynucleotide chain can be demonstrated experimentally without much difficulty and then interpreted as "dissociation" of subunits, which are presumed to exist under natural conditions.

In our experiments, we were able to isolate ribosomal RNA from diverse types of cells (bacterial, animal and plant) which were shown not to dissociate either on heating or on removal of the bivalent and multivalent metallic cations (Spirin, 1961a). All these RNA preparations showed a manifold increase in specific activity caused by the rupture of hydrogen bonds and by thermal unfolding of the polynucleotide chains. "Versene," in high concentrations, had no apparent effect on this rise. Ribosomal RNA from *E. coli* displayed an unfolding of the chains (80° C) when heated over 5- or 15-minute intervals. On cooling, the original molecule dimensions were fully restored in both the large and the small components (23S and 17S) of this ribosomal RNA (Bogdanova et al., 1962). Finally, long continuous threads of ribosomal RNA, in an uncoiled state, were seen under the electron microscope, some of them measuring up to 18,000 Å in length, as shown in the micrographs of ribosomal RNA. This apparently corresponded to a single continuous uncoiled polynucleotide chain constituting the large component in a ribosomal RNA particle. Its molecular weight amounted to about 1.1×10^6 (Kiselev et al., 1961b; Bogdanova et al., 1962). According to these data, either constituent of any ribosomal RNA molecule, whether the small or the large component, appears to consist of a single continuous polynucleotide chain, which unfolds, but does not dissociate, when heated, causing a marked thickening of the solution, and then easily folds back, resuming its original shape on cooling.

From such evidence it may be inferred that what was described as a dissociation of RNA in numerous reports was a condition resulting either from contamination of the RNA preparation with nucleases or from an excessively harsh thermal treatment which caused degradation of the chain. It could also indicate a poor quality of the preparations, which may have consisted of RNA particles with previously damaged chains.

Recently all experimental results supporting the concept of subunits were rechecked at Doty's laboratory. When a thoroughly purified RNA, containing no nuclease admixtures, was tested in the presence of polyvinyl sulfate (a strong inhibitor of ribonuclease), the removal of metal, whether by dialysis or by adding protein to the ribosomal RNA, did not in itself cause a dissociation of the macromolecule (Möller and Boedtker, 1961, 1962; Boedtker et al., 1962). These authors were able to demonstrate that the phenomenon described by Aronson and McCarthy, as well as by Brown and co-workers (see above) as a dissociation of the RNA molecule into subunits, was actually an enzymic degradation which developed in a preparation contaminated with traces of nucleases. The same authors (Möller and Boedtker, 1962; Boedtker et al., 1962) repeated the earlier experiments carried out at Doty's laboratory (Hall and Doty, 1958, 1959). The kinetics of heat degradation affecting an RNA macromolecule was studied. It was concluded that heating of an RNA solution causes a simple random thermal rupture of the polynucleotide RNA chain, rather than a dissociation into subunits. Magnesium ions were found to catalyze strongly such thermal degradation. Most recently, Bock and Stanley (1962) verified the data of Helmkamp and Ts'o. On treating ribosomal RNA from *E. coli* with formamide or dimethyl sulfoxide, they noted no dissociation of the RNA molecule. Nor were they able to observe this effect following a thorough removal of bivalent and multivalent metal cations from ribosomal RNA preparations by means of special complex-forming (chelating) resins. On the basis of these results, Bock and Stanley now fully subscribe to the view that ribosomal RNA possesses a "continuous structure held together by covalent bonds, with no ruptured links in the chain." Thus the theory of continuous chains as the structural basis of high-polymeric RNA, whether of virus or ribosomal origin, advanced in our earlier reports (Spirin, 1960, 1961a; Spirin and Mil'man, 1960) is being amply confirmed by current studies.

At one time, however, Boedtker, Möller and Doty, it will be noted (Boedtker et al., 1961; Doty, 1961), reported the continuity of polynucleotide chains for molecules of the small compound only (16S), averaging about 500,000 in molecular weight. The constituent particles of the large component in ribosomal RNA (23S), according to their communication, were dimers of the 16S component. On removal of magnesium ions with the aid of ion-exchange resins or by means of dialysis, they found that only the 16S component remained intact, while the 23S component dissociated (into two 16S, as claimed in the report). After increasing the magnesium concentration and adding spermidine, the authors found that the 16S components could again become dimerized, and in fact trimerized. In our own experiments, as mentioned earlier, thermal unfolding of the chains in ribosomal RNA was effected by heating the solution to 80° C in the presence of "Versene" in substantial concentrations. The tests demonstrated a complete restoration of the sedimentation pattern on cooling of the solution (Bogdanova et al., 1962). No dissociation of the 23S component into 16S components was found to result from the unfolding of chains, hydrogen bond rupture, or magnesium removal. Our results were cited by the above authors (Doty, Boedtker, Möller) from a direct statement made by us in the relevant reports (Spirin 1961b, 1962b). At the present time, the

Doty and Boedtker group fully adhere to the view that the polynucleotide chain in the 23S component of ribosomal RNA is continuous. Some evidence confirming the validity of this concept has been obtained by them in recent experiments (Boedtker et al., 1962; Möller and Boedtker, 1962). The occasional "dissociation" of this component into two lesser ones was found to represent in reality a degradation of the chain.

The overall conclusion from these observational data, as described, is that the ribosomal RNA molecules, as in the case of virus RNA, consist of long continuous polynucleotide chains. In small components, depending on their molecular weights, the chains are composed of 1500-2000 nucleotides held together by covalent forces. The chain in a large component is made up of as many as 4000-4500 nucleotide residues. The possibility that some continuous chains may comprise up to 6000 nucleotides cannot be ruled out at this time.

c) "Soluble" RNA

Molecular weight measurements by physicochemical methods (see Chapter II, 1, b; Tissieres, 1959; Brown and Zubay, 1960; Cox and Littauer, 1960; Okawa, 1960) as well as chain-length determinations based on the end-group technique (Hecht et al., 1958; Dunn, 1959; Dunn et al., 1960; Singer and Cantoni, Allen et al., 1960, Habermann, 1960) indicate that the molecules of "soluble" RNA should be viewed as continuous polynucleotide chains which, according to the larger portion of currently available data, consist of 80-100 nucleotide residues held together by covalent bonds. A different concept, in which the "soluble" RNA particle is envisaged as a double chain molecule, was proposed by Zilly and co-workers (1960). According to their measurements, the molecular weight of "soluble" RNA, calculated from sedimentation and diffusion data, equaled 35,000 while chain-length determinations by chemical methods yielded an average length, for a single chain, corresponding to a molecular weight of 18,500 (60 nucleotides). A still lower average chain—length as little as 40 nucleotides—was obtained for "soluble" RNA by Herbert and Canellakis (1960). Preiss et al. (1959), on the other hand, reported far larger values for "soluble" RNA molecules, up to 50,000, as based on chain measurements. Apparently, average chain-length determinations by chemical methods involving end groups may easily prove inaccurate, owing to the presence of RNA degradation products along with various oligonucleotides, or else of admixtures containing high-polymeric RNA and fragments. In any event, sufficient data are now available to indicate that molecular weights computed for "soluble" RNA from chain-length measurements, as determined by physicochemical methods, are in close agreement. It could hardly be doubted, furthermore, that every molecule of "soluble" RNA consists of a single continuous chain.

Chapter III

CONFORMATION OF RNA CHAINS IN SOLUTION

Early studies on the isolation of native RNA, specifically high-polymeric RNA, date back to the years when the Watson-Crick structural model representing the macromolecular structure of DNA received general recognition and was confirmed by numerous experimental data. These advances left their imprint on the refinement of theoretical concepts depicting the macromolecular structure of RNA. Considering the extreme similarity in chemical properties between these two classes of nucleic acids, along with the fact that the very first experiments yielded remarkably close values for the respective molecular weights of DNA and high-polymeric RNA, the investigators had practically no alternative but to assume for RNA a structure of a double-stranded helix type, as proposed by Watson-Crick. This trend was bolstered by experiments on synthesizing regular double-stranded helical polyribonucleotide complexes of the type poly (A + U), poly (A + A), etc. (Rich and Davis, 1956; Felsenfeld and Rich, 1957; Warner, 1957; Fresco and Doty, 1957). Some experiments on RNA titration (Cox et al., 1956), along with preliminary X-ray structural data (Rich and Watson, 1954a, b) pointed, in fact, to certain Watson-Crick elements as part of the RNA structure. All this, however, was contradicted by extensive analytical data on the nucleotide composition of RNA, which made evident the lack of consistent pairing of purine with pyrimidine, guanine with cytosine, or adenine with uracil (see Magasanik, 1955; Elson and Chargaff, 1955, Belozerskii and Spirin, 1960).

More direct data, which showed that the RNA structure does not appear to be analogous to the double-stranded structure of native DNA, were first obtained for biologically active, infectious RNA from TMV. Gierer (1957) isolated infectious virus RNA and studied the kinetics of its degradation when acted upon by pancreatic ribonuclease. He found that each individual step in the enzymic splitting of a phosphodiester leads to a decrease in molecular weight, i.e., to a degradation of the molecule. It was further established that the entire kinetics of the degradation discloses the splitting of a single-stranded chain, rather than of a double-stranded, DNA-like chain. Gierer's data were confirmed in an independent study of Ginoza (1958, 1959) as he followed up the kinetics of thermal degradation in tests on virus RNA in solution. Each consecutive disintegration of an RNA molecule in the course of thermal degradation resulted from the hydrolysis involving a single internucleotide bond, so that the degradation kinetics was expressed by an equation of the first order.

At about the same time, Hart (1958) carried out an electron microscope study of virus RNA with complementary mathematical analysis. When deposited on a collodion substrate, the virus RNA was seen to have the form of a long thread, about 10 Å in diameter, corresponding to a single-stranded polyribonucleotide chain. An attempt was made, furthermore, to evaluate the amount of RNA contained in a TMV particle in relation to an estimated length of the RNA molecule, as based on its shape when packed inside the virus particle. According to Hart's calculations, a double-stranded chain could not have the proper length to fit into a TMV particle. Conversely, an unwound single-stranded chain was shown to meet such requirements as are imposed by the virus particle structure.

A single-strand chain structure was subsequently demonstrated for high-polymeric cellular RNA. First, Gierer (1958a), in a study of RNA isolated from the microsomes of rat liver and from tobacco leaves, found that in either case the kinetics of degradation, under the action of ribonuclease, followed the same pattern as that determined earlier for virus RNA, i.e., the equations expressed the degradation of a single-chain molecule.

Later, identical relationships between molecular weight, sedimentation coefficient and characteristic or specific viscosity were established for various RNA preparations, of both virus and ribosomal origin, at several laboratories. Such relationships differed from those known to apply in the case of the rigid, filamentary, double-stranded DNA molecules. Rather, a similarity was displayed to the case of compact, coiled particles (Gierer, 1958a, c; Hall and Doty, 1958, 1959; Boedtker, 1959). It was further evidenced by extensive hydrodynamic data (viscosity and sedimentation) that in contradistinction to the rigid structure of DNA, the RNA particles behave like flexible molecules, which undergo smoothly developing, reversible changes in the shape and linear dimensions when affected by the ionic strength of the solution (Gierer, 1958a, c; Eisenberg and Littauer, 1958; Hall and Doty, 1958, 1959; Boedtker, 1959; Littauer and Eisenberg, 1959). The RNA behaved like a flexible, single-stranded, contractible polyelectrolyte, whose specific viscosity varied within wide limits depending on the salt concentration in the solution.

The number of hydrogen bonds in RNA molecules was likewise reported to vary smoothly and reversibly with the ionic strength, pH and temperature of the solution. Such behavior was the opposite of that noted for DNA (Spirin and Gavrilova, 1958; Spirin, Gavrilova and Belozersky, 1959a; Hall and Doty, 1958, 1959; Boedtker, 1959; Littauer and Eisenberg, 1959).

Thus, the sum total of experimental evidence led to the conclusion that RNA in solution is structurally distinct from the rigid, double-stranded molecules of the DNA type, being built essentially of flexible single-stranded polyribonucleotide chains wound into compact particles while in solution. These particles undergo reversible changes in shape, size and the number of intramolecular hydrogen bonds, depending on conditions specified for the solution (ionic strength, pH, presence of urea, temperature, etc.).

The first question to be considered in studying the polynucleotide RNA chain in solution was whether it was a simple, flexible, single-stranded polymer having no distinctly oriented conformation (a randomly oriented coil) or whether the macromolecular organization of polymeric RNA differed from a random chain orientation.

In 1959, some data were published for the first time and interpreted as evidence that the molecules of high-polymeric RNA in solution possess an oriented structure, which "melts" at higher temperatures within a definite interval (Doty et al., 1959; Gavrilova et al., 1959; Spirin, Gavrilova, Bresler and Mosevitskiy, 1959). In our first communication published in June 1959, we reported the discovery of a "temperature effect" noted for high-polymeric RNA (see above). Analysis of changes in hydrodynamic properties (sedimentation and viscosity) disclosed an abrupt structural transformation of the RNA molecules following a rise of the solution temperature. In the transition, the compact molecules became uncoiled, i.e., the particle as a whole assumed a different configuration (Gavrilova et al., 1959; Spirin, Gavrilova, Bresler and Mosevitskiy, 1959). The Doty team (April 1959) studied a different set of RNA properties involving hyperchromicity and optical activity. Such optical characteristics were likewise shown to change regularly at higher temperatures of solution. The same kind of changes was discovered in an independent study carried out by us jointly with S. E. Bresler's laboratory in 1959. A report describing this work was published somewhat later than Doty's paper (December 1959). The change pattern indicated a structural transition associated with intramolecular transformations, involving a reversible thermal destruction of the helical structures in the RNA molecules.

In the same year, it was reported that similar transitions, evidencing an oriented state of polynucleotide RNA chains in salt-containing solutions, are observed even on lowering the ionic strength of solution. Such observations were recorded for both virus RNA (Haschemeyer et al., 1959) and ribosomal RNA (Cox and Littauer, 1959).

Chain conformation in any oriented polymeric molecule can be conveniently depicted and analyzed at two different levels. One level involves the possible regularities and periodicity in the spatial arrangement of adjacent monomers and neighboring chain links; the other level concerns the regularities and specific arrangement pattern for the chain packed inside the molecule as a whole. The first level in the spatial orientation of a polymer is customarily designated as the secondary structure. The term implies primarily some type of helical structure assumed by the chain and held together by hydrogen bonds. The second level is defined as the tertiary structure, which may be either periodic or uniquely aperiodic, but in all cases depends on electrostatic, van der Waals and other weak intramolecular bonds acting between individual links and areas of the chain-shaped molecule.

1. HELICAL SECTIONS (SECONDARY STRUCTURE)

The polymeric nucleic acids, DNA and RNA, have long been known to have far lower respective values of specific ultraviolet (UV) absorption than could be expected on the basis of a simple summation of absorption values for each of the constituent nucleotides (hypochromicity of nucleic acids). Attempts to trace the causes of hypochromicity, in experiments with native DNA, indicated a direct correlation between the magnitude of this effect and the number of specific hydrogen bonds linking the ends of the two polynucleotide chains wound spirally about each other, which form the DNA molecule (Thomas, 1954; Laland et al., 1954; Beaven et al., 1955; Duggan et al., 1957; others). Rupture of the hydrogen bonds and DNA denaturation lead to a considerable intensification of UV absorption ("hyperchromic effect"). An identical regularity pattern was demonstrated for synthetic polynucleotide complexes with a helical structure (Felsenfeld and Rich, 1957; Warner, 1957; Fresco and Doty, 1957; others). Hypochromicity in molecules of the polynucleotide type was thus found to be directly associated with an oriented helical structure held together by hydrogen bonds (secondary structure). It could be expected, therefore, that a study of UV hypochromicity in high-polymeric RNA would yield important information concerning the presence, and nature, of the secondary structure in the macromolecules of these acids. Before 1959, however, no positive data were available on the secondary structure of RNA, although a strong hypochromic effect displayed by high-polymeric RNA in solution was mentioned in many reports (Hopkins and Sinsheimer, 1955; Gierer and Schramm, 1956a, b; Gierer 1957, 1958a; Reddi, 1958; Hall and Doty, 1958).

In studying the secondary structure of polypeptides and proteins, the basic experimental procedure was concerned with another group of optical properties, namely, their capacity to rotate the plane of polarized light (optical activity). The experiments, conducted first on simple polypeptides and then on native proteins, led to an important discovery. It was found that helical chain structure causes a strong optical rotation, in addition to the optical activity associated with the presence of asymmetric carbon atoms in the amino acid residues (Doty et al., 1954; Doty and Lundberg, 1957; Doty, 1959a, b). At the same time, it became known from the studies of Gierer (1957, 1958a) that native RNA, when in solution, possesses a strong optical activity. It rotates the plane of polarization to the right, while neither its constituent nucleotides nor the degraded virus RNA exhibits such a high capacity for optical rotation.

By 1958-1959 it had thus been established (1) that hypochromicity, in the case of native DNA and of synthetic dimeric and trimeric polynucleotide complexes, is the result of their helical structure, upheld by hydrogen bonds; (2) that native high-polymeric RNA in solution displays a considerable hypochromic effect; (3) that polypeptide chains of a helical structure acquire a capacity for strong optical rotation; (4) that native high-polymeric RNA in solution is strongly dextrorotatory, while its constituent nucleotides themselves are capable of negligible optical rotation.

Our data on the "temperature effect" in virus RNA, obtained in early 1959, indicated that the structure of this acid had some degree of orientation (Gavrilova et al., 1959). This suggested that the elements of helical structure in the RNA macromolecules may be at least partly responsible for the orientation pattern. With this assumption in mind, and considering the evidence of hypochromicity and optical activity in virus RNA, we studied these properties at various temperatures, correlating them with the dynamics of the "temperature effect" (Spirin, Gavrilova, Bresler, Mosevitskiy, 1959). The study was subsequently extended to ribosomal RNA, *E. coli* being chosen as the RNA source (Bogdanova et al., 1962).

For the study of UV absorption at 260 mμ and of optical rotation at 589 mμ (the D line of sodium), we used solutions in a phosphate buffer or in a tris buffer, ionic strength 0.1, pH 7.2. We also used a 6 *M* urea solution buffered with phosphate to the same ionic strength and to the same pH. At room temperature (20° C) both RNA's under consideration—from virus and from ribosomes—exhibited considerable hypochromicity, and the respective values obtained for the two acids were quite close (UV absorption for RNA was less by 30–35% than the value found for a mixture of mononucleotides equivalent to either RNA preparation). Under these conditions, the molar extinction at 260 mμ, calculated per 1 gram atom of phosphorus—$\epsilon(P)_{260}$—amounted to 7850 for virus RNA and 7900 for ribosomal RNA isolated from *E. coli*. The value of specific optical rotation, at 589 mμ—$[\alpha]_D^{20}$— was equal for both acids (+170°). On introduction of urea into the solutions (up to a concentration of 6 *M*) the value of UV absorption, for both RNA, increased up to $\epsilon(P)_{260}$ = 8700–8900, while specific optical rotation decreased to +145°. Thus urea, an agent exerting a specific effect on hydrogen bonds, was found to influence simultaneously both properties—hypochromicity and optical activity. This indicated, in the first place, that both indices apparently reflect the same structural feature in the RNA molecules and, secondly, that this feature is associated with the effect of intramolecular hydrogen bonds. The close similarity of indices obtained for virus and ribosomal RNA suggested further that this structural feature is common to both types of high-polymeric RNA under study.

In Fig. 7 are shown characteristic curves in which UV absorption and specific optical rotation values, for high-polymeric RNA, are plotted against temperature. It is above all apparent from these data that an intensification of UV absorption (hyperchromic effect) and a decline of optical rotation take place, in fact, more or less concurrently with the abrupt change in hydrodynamic values ("temperature effect"; see Fig. 6). When the solution is cooled to the original temperature, it will be noted that the UV absorption and optical rotation values, along with the initial vis-

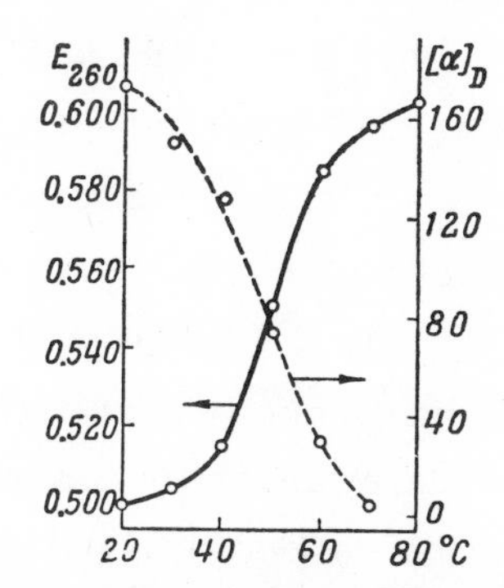

Fig. 7. Specific optical rotation and UV absorption curves plotted against temperature, for ribosomal RNA (from *E. coli*) in 0.1 *M* tris buffer, pH 7.2 (Bogdanova et al., 1962).

cosity and sedimentation coefficients, are completely restored. This means that the strong dextrorotatory optical activity and considerable hypochromicity of high-polymeric RNA are associated solely with a particular configuration. Consequently, any change in structural factors responsible for the hypochromicity and optical activity is somehow involved in the transition from orientation to disorientation, as reflected in the "temperature effect." The respective curves for the decline in optical rotation and the intensification of UV absorption are closely similar in shape and, therefore, appear to reflect changes in the same structural factor.

It has been known for some time that spiralization of polynucleotides could be such a structural factor, responsible simultaneously for hypochromicity and high optical activity of a purely configurational origin. It is further known that heating leads to a rupture of the hydrogen bonds which uphold the helical structure of polynucleotides; hence, it must result in a transition from a helical to a disoriented state of the chains. This is obviously a transition of the "orientation-disorientation" type. The overall conclusion is that in experiments with heated RNA solutions we observe a transition of the RNA molecules from one state to another, accompanied by despiralization of the polynucleotide chain or of some sections of it.

It follows that the structural orientation that is characteristic of the RNA molecule at room temperature finds a concrete expression, at least partially, in the presence of helical structures supported by hydrogen bonds (secondary structure). Such a secondary structure undergoes a reversible disintegration following a rise of temperature, but is restored once the original conditions have been re-established. It should be pointed out that the presence of 6 *M* urea in the solution enhances the disintegration of the helices in the RNA. This is further evidence that the oriented areas of the chain, which are responsible for the hypochromicity and optical activity of RNA, are supported by hydrogen bonds and are therefore elements of the secondary structure.

The author has mentioned elsewhere a paper describing the effect of heating on optical activity and UV absorption in virus RNA (Spirin, Gavrilova, Bresler, Mosevitskiy, 1959). A few months earlier in the same year, Doty and co-workers published a report concerned specifically with a detailed study of the secondary structure in high-polymeric RNA—predominantly virus RNA (from TMV)—in solution. The results of these investigations, carried out independently of each other, are in complete agreement with respect to some of the observed phenomena. In both sets of experiments, a decline in optical rotation was noted on heating, with simultaneous intensification of UV absorption. Furthermore, both research teams reached the same general conclusions affirming the existence of secondary structures (helices supported by hydrogen bonds). At the same time, Doty and his collaborators were able to explore the problem much more thoroughly and in far greater detail. Their concepts regarding the nature and structure of the helical areas as such are more clearly defined. What is more, they succeeded in formulating some conclusions of a quantitative nature. Subsequent research conducted at Doty's laboratory and related studies by Fresco yielded even more detailed data on the secondary structure of RNA, which were further refined (Fresco and Alberts, 1960; Alberts and Doty, 1960). At the present time, this basic exploratory work provides a foundation upon which our concepts are being developed as regards the actual nature of the secondary structure presumed for RNA in solution.

By now, studies of optical rotation and UV hypochromicity have demonstrated the presence of helical structures in RNA molecules, for preparations of different origin, kept in solutions of not too low ionic strength, at room temperature. This was shown to be true in the case of virus RNA (Doty et al., 1959a, b; Spirin, Gavrilova, Bresler, Mosevitskiy, 1959), ribosomal RNA (Doty et al., 1959a, b; Littauer, 1961; Helmkamp and Ts'o, 1961; Bogdanova et al., 1962) and "soluble" RNA (Tissieres, 1959; Brown and Zubay, 1960; Cox and Littauer, 1960; Littauer, 1961; Kiselev et al., 1962a, b). It was further demonstrated that the helical structures existing in the RNA molecules, when in solution, are supported by hydrogen bonds acting between the nitrogenous bases of the chain. Raising the temperature of the solution causes a thermal rupture of the hydrogen bonds, followed by disintegration of the helices ("melting" of the secondary structure). This is reflected in a diminution of optical rotation nearly to zero, with simultaneous intensification of specific UV absorption (see Fig. 7). It was found that a similar disintegration of the helical structures could be achieved by transferring the RNA into aqueous solutions entirely free of salts, into acid or alkaline solutions, or into solvents such as formamide and dimethyl sulfoxide. All measurements performed on RNA from widely diversified sources, including virus, ribosomal and "soluble" RNA, reveal a close similarity in the basic characteristics of the secondary structure.

At the same time, distinctive properties of the secondary structure, demonstrated experimentally for RNA, differ strongly from those in DNA. The latter acid is a continuous, perfect, double-stranded helix, which imparts rigidity to the molecule along its entire length. In the case of RNA, however, the possibility of such a single rigid helical structure must be ruled out, in view of the hydrodynamic properties of this acid.

The RNA molecule, furthermore, is found to be a single continuous polynucleotide chain. This means that no secondary structure can emerge in RNA except as a result of interaction between the links of the same chain. (The DNA molecule, on the other hand, is made up of two chains, which can be separated by denaturation.) It follows that the spiralization of the RNA chain, unlike that of DNA, can be brought about only by the interaction of the bases within the chain.

Another distinction relates to the complete and practically instantaneous reversibility of both the thermal disintegration ("melting") of helices and the rupture of hydrogen bonds, as noted for the RNA molecule. The same process in the case of DNA (denaturation) is partially reversible only under special conditions of slow cooling (renaturation).

The most important distinction, observed in all experiments on the "melting" of helical structures in RNA, is the absence of an abrupt transition within a narrow temperature range, characteristic of the DNA molecules. The abruptness of transition indicates a coordinated simultaneous disintegration involving the whole of a single, regular unitary structure. In the case of RNA, a transition is possible within an incomparably wider temperature range than is required for "melting" a single helix of the DNA type. An RNA transition reflects rather a successive independent melting of numerous separate short helices.

From the sum total of such experimental observations it was concluded that the spiralization of an RNA molecule is not complete, as it is in DNA, but partial, and that the secondary structure of RNA in solution is most likely an assembly of relatively short helices which appear as hydrogen bonds are formed between the bases of one and the same chain (Doty et al., 1959; Spirin, Gavrilova, Bresler, Mosevitskiy, 1959; Fresco et al., 1960; Spirin, 1960). The concept of the secondary RNA structure is based on the assumption that the spiralization in the RNA molecule results from intramolecular interaction inside one single-stranded chain and is promoted by the action of the hydrogen bonds linking the nitrogenous bases of this chain.

The Doty team showed that the individual areas of the polynucleotide chain in the RNA molecule most probably interact with one another in pairs (Doty et al., 1959). The assumption seems plausible, considering that a single-stranded RNA chain is highly flexible so that different chain areas can come into contact with one another. The areas in contact interact, because their bases are linked in pairs by the hydrogen bonds. Some areas in the chain become spirally wound about each other, with the result that a local double-stranded helical formation appears at the site. Since a very large number of contacts are possible between various areas of a single-stranded chain inside the molecule of high-polymeric RNA, the latter becomes nearly saturated with newly formed double-stranded helical areas, distributed at random within the RNA particle, as shown by Doty et al. (1959) and Boedtker (1959, 1960).

Such mutual spiralization of two polynucleotide areas may result from the hydrogen bonding (pairing) of two bases. Pairs of widely varied types may be involved, including purine-pyrimidine, purine-purine, and pyrimidine-pyrimidine. If we consider the steric laws, however, it will be apparent that none of these double helices can be of a mixed type so far as the pairing of bases is concerned. (Each of the three pairs indicated above requires a specific distance between the carcass chains of the two paired areas.) It can be expected, therefore, that in any helical region only one type of base pairing will be found—either pyrimidine-pyrimidine, purine-purine, or, as in DNA, purine-pyrimidine. Doty and co-workers reported various data demonstrating that the last-mentioned type of pairing is the only one (or, at any rate, the predominant type) actually observed in the RNA molecules (Doty et al., 1959; Fresco et al., 1960). It was further claimed that all, or practically all, pairing activity within an RNA molecule, when in solution at room temperature, results from interaction of adenine with uracil and guanine with cytosine (the AU pairs and GC pairs). The helical areas in RNA molecules form as the chain, or some sections of it, fold upon themselves. Hence, the strands in any helical region will not run in parallel (Doty et al., 1959; Fresco et al., 1960). This indicates that individual helical areas in RNA display some characteristic DNA traits, such as the AU and GC pairs, along with nonparallel strands.

X-ray structural studies of different RNA preparations (virus, ribosomal and "soluble") fully confirmed the presence in RNA of double-stranded helices similar to those in DNA (Rich and Watson, 1954a, b; Brown and Zubay, 1960; Zubay and Wilkins, 1960; Klug et al., 1961; Spencer et al., 1962). A study of major significance, in this connection, was reported by Spencer, Fuller, Wilkins and Brown (Spencer et al., 1962). Theirs were the first experiments on record in which a partially crystallized preparation of "soluble" RNA was successfully isolated from yeast. They were also able to obtain X-ray pictures which made it possible to define more closely the structural characteristics of helices in RNA. The authors noted a close resemblance, excepting a few minor differences, between the roentgenograms obtained for a crystalline sample of the tested RNA and for DNA in a crystalline A-form. A spatial model representing an RNA helix was constructed to scale, on the basis of the diffraction pictures obtained. Significantly, the helical structure established by the authors for a sample of crystalline "soluble" RNA is in excellent agreement with the diffuse X-ray pictures of high-polymeric RNA. This facilitates the interpretation both of earlier X-ray structural data and of the results reported in the above communication on noncrystallizable ribosomal and virus RNA. The same authors conclude that "all types of RNA contain helical areas, whose configuration is basically similar to that of DNA in the A-form" (Spencer et al., 1962).

Thus, the helical areas in RNA are formed by sections of the same single-stranded polyribonucleotide chain, and therefore assume a double-stranded (double helix) shape similar to that found in DNA. All, or nearly all, helical regions in the RNA macromolecule are supported by hydrogen bonds linking adenine and uracil (one doublet of hydrogen bonds per one pair of interacting bases) as well as guanine and cytosine (one triplet of hydrogen bonds per one pair of interacting bases).

Data on the "melting" temperature of the secondary RNA structure are quite consistent with the view which presumes the pairing of guanine with cytosine and of adenine with uracil to be a basic feature of this structure. Fresco and co-workers (1960) cite some unpublished observations of Fresco and Givelber, testifying to the existence of a linear correlation between the thermal stability of various RNA and the GC content in these acids. In our experiments (Spirin, 1961a) numerous preparations of high-polymeric RNA were tested, including those from TMV, *E. coli*, pea seedlings, bone marrow of rabbits, and rat liver. All these showed an identical picture of thermal unfolding, revealed as a sharp increase in specific viscosity, except that the midpoint of such uncoiling lay at various temperature levels, depending on the nature of the preparation (see Fig. 6). This mean temperature of thermal unfolding was found to be linearly correlated specifically with the GC content in the RNA (Fig. 8). From these results it was inferred that all the other characteristics of the secondary and tertiary structures of RNA in solution, which could affect the total thermal stability of RNA conformations, appear to be common to RNA of different origin (Spirin, 1961a). (Such characteristics included the extent of spiralization, the length of the helical areas, the average relative value of defective areas, the coiling arrangement, etc.)

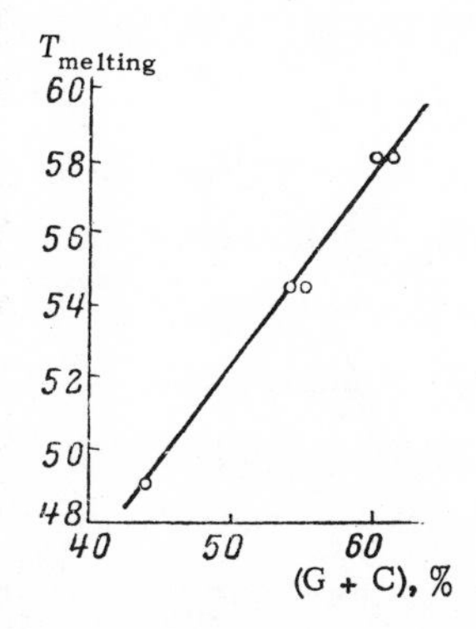

Fig. 8. Temperature of thermal unfolding as a function of the nucleotide composition in high-polymeric RNA of different origin (TMV, *E. coli*, pea seedlings, rabbit and rat tissues).
Abscissa—Molar content of the sum of guanine plus cytosine (G + C) as percentage of total base content. Ordinate—Mean temperature of thermal unfolding of chain ($T_{melting}$) based on viscosimetric data (Spirin, 1961a).

Differences in the mean "melting" temperature for various secondary structures, as determined from UV absorption measurements, were noted also by Wallace and Ts'o (1961) in experiments with ribosomal RNA from pea seedlings and reticulocytes of rabbits and sheep. The temperature value was shown to vary with the GC content in the RNA preparations.

The extent of spiralization in the RNA molecules was evaluated quantitatively (i.e., the percentage of the total number of nucleotides in the RNA chain which became organized into areas of helical structure). This was accomplished by contrasting the values of specific optical rotation and UV hypochromicity obtained for RNA with respective values for a completely spiralized double-stranded complex of polyadenylic plus polyuridylic acids—poly (AU) (Doty et al., 1959). If the value of, say, $[\alpha_D^{20}]$ for RNA approximated +170°, while for poly (AU) under identical conditions it equaled +300°, then the extent of circumvolution in RNA amounted to about 50-60%. This meant that some 50-60% of all nucleotide residues in the RNA chain had become organized into helical areas supported by hydrogen bonds, while the remaining 40-50% of nucleotides in the chain were located outside the helices. This extent of spiralization for the RNA molecules in solution was further confirmed by other methods based on the kinetics of the formaldehyde reaction, of phosphorolysis, etc. (Doty et al., 1959). In more recent experiments (Doty, 1961) the above data were refined on the basis of evidence obtained from comparative studies of hypochromicity as a function of the nucleotide RNA composition. The author came to the conclusion that the extent of spiralization in the molecules of high-polymeric RNA is even higher than shown by earlier results. According to his data, the spiralized nucleotides totaled 84% in

RNA from TMV and 78% in ribosomal RNA from liver tissue. These figures are at variance with the most recent data of Fresco on spiralization, which is shown not to exceed 70%.

As to the size (length) of such helical areas in RNA, it follows from the same investigations (Doty et al., 1959) that the helices, at any rate, cannot be very long. From the data obtained, notably the estimated transition temperature range and the melting temperature of helices, it would seem that the secondary RNA structure is an aggregation of fairly diversified, short helical regions distributed throughout the RNA particle. A more detailed analysis of this matter will be found in a later report (Fresco et al., 1960). The smallest RNA helices were shown to comprise 4-6 pairs of nucleotides (about one-half of a complete coil in a double helix). Most helices, however, appeared to be longer, so that the average size of a helix could be taken to measure one full coil (10 pairs of nucleotides).

The nucleotide residues in an RNA chain which have not been organized into helices, most likely constitute the nonspiralized, disoriented areas in the single-stranded chain that link the spiralized areas, or form loops in places where the chain makes a U-turn. Quite possibly, some of the nonspiralized nucleotides may be located inside the spiralized regions. In such cases, being noncomplementary to the antipodal neighbors, they protrude as mono- or binucleotide loops (Fresco and Alberts, 1960). Such "defects" in helical areas can be seen in Fig. 9 (schematic diagram taken from the report by Fresco et al., 1960). It follows that helical regions in the RNA molecules are not necessarily DNA-like formations of a purely helical configuration but may occasionally have the form of imperfect (defective) helices. This type of organization in the helical areas makes possible the mutual spiralization of chain areas which are not fully complementary, thus considerably widening the scope of spiralization inside the RNA molecule. Even in the case of a random sequence of nucleotides, the extent of spiralization may be as high as 50%, if the model representing "helices with loops" is accepted as plausible (Fresco et al., 1960). Such evidence, demonstrating that the "defective helix" formation is possible, served to explain the factual high percentage of spiralization in RNA, without assuming some unique regularity pattern in the nucleotide sequence.

The secondary structure, for a nucleotide chain consisting of 90 nucleotides, as conceived by Fresco, Alberts and Doty (Fresco et al., 1960) is shown schematically in Fig. 10. In the diagram, imperfect (defective) short helices approximating one full coil (10 pairs of nucleotides) in length are seen to alternate with nonspiralized, disoriented areas of the same chain.

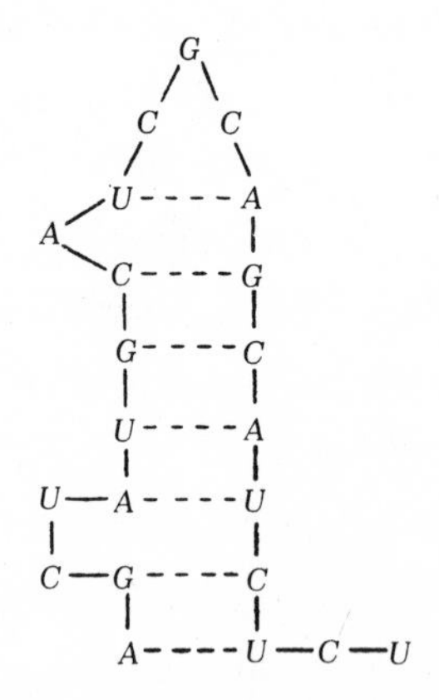

Fig. 9. A double-stranded polynucleotide helix with "loops" formed by unpaired nucleotides (Fresco et al., 1960).

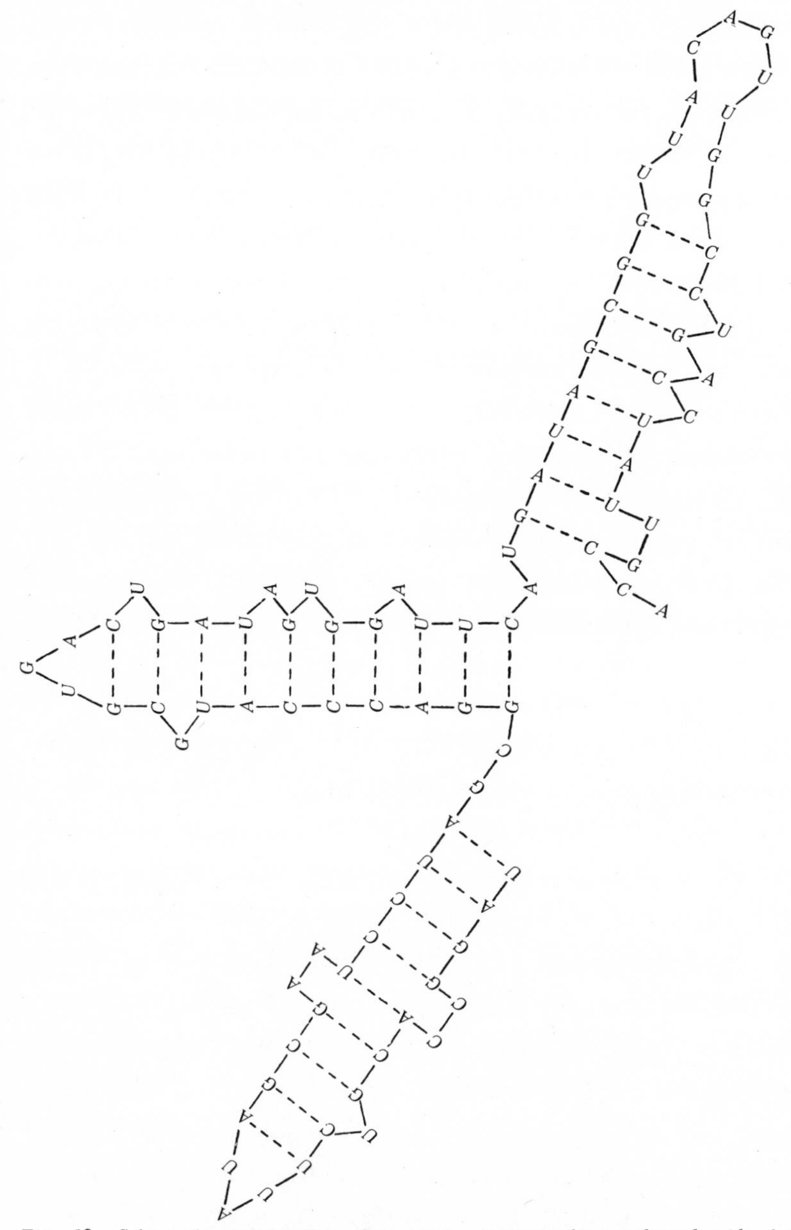

Fig. 10. Schematic presentation of seconary structure for a polynucleotide chain consisting of 90 nucleotides (Fresco et al., 1960).

A subsequent report by the same authors (Fresco et al., 1961) described the results of a preliminary study on rotational dispersion of RNA in the UV region of the spectrum. It was thought possible that "native RNA possesses a more extensively developed and precise secondary structure, such as would occur if the helical regions were longer and contained fewer defects." This conclusion apparently requires further verification.

Of considerable interest, in this connection, are the studies of Luzzati and co-workers (Timashev et al., 1961) on X-ray diffraction at small angles in RNA solutions. The experimental results, as seen by the authors, suggested that the RNA molecule in solution consists of rigid, rod-shaped segments interlinked by flexible areas. Each segment is presumed likely to be constituted as a double-stranded helical structure of a DNA type. These concepts are on the whole consistent with the secondary structure model discussed above, except for two important points in which they differ from the concept developed by the Fresco team. First, the mean length for the rigid rod-shaped sections, as estimated by Luzzati and co-workers, is much greater, amounting to about 100 Å (from 50 to 150 Å). Second, the rod-shaped segments, according to the same authors, take up at least 90% of the entire RNA structure (i.e., the RNA molecule is assumed to be almost completely spiralized). The authors believe, therefore, that the specific pairs of bases, AU and GC, are not indispensable for spiralization and that other pairs may be involved in the formation of RNA helices.

Whatever the case may be, the secondary RNA structure apparently should not be visualized as a rigidly predetermined, fixed native formation. Quite the contrary, it is a typical, balanced, reversible structure. As the actual conditions in the solutions vary, the RNA chain spontaneously assumes some specific conformation which for the given conditions corresponds to a state of equilibrium attained by the various molecular forces. This is true for RNA from TMV, as pointed out specifically in our report (Spirin, Gavrilova, Bresler, Mosevitskiy, 1959). The high-polymeric RNA, in a TMV particle, consists of a chain held together by the protein components of the virus, in the shape of a regular low-angle spiral, with a 23 Å pitch, 80 Å in diameter. This conformation has no kinship whatever with the secondary structure under consideration. After deproteinization of TMV, the RNA chain, now in a free state, acquires spontaneously the characteristic secondary structure of any RNA in solution.

It was demonstrated by Felsenfeld (1958), in earlier experiments on synthesized proteins serving as models, that the complementary pairing of polyribonucleotide chains, or sections thereof, involves specifically a reversible interaction. This makes possible a lateral motion of the chains, or their sections, relative to one another, which continues until the most advantageous energy state has been attained. Fresco and Alberts (1960) reached the conclusion, based likewise on experimenting with model polynucleotides, that in the case where the elements are not fully complementary, an essential feature of the groping lateral motion is the mutual adjustment of the chains, or sections of chains, which is accomplished with the aid of loops formed by the noncomplementary nucleotides.

Bearing this in mind, the Fresco team (1960) assumed as a basic proposition to be guided by when considering the RNA structure in solution that RNA acquires its most stable conformation as the result of lateral mobility, which enables it to seek, and find, the most effective of all competing configurations. Complete, and practically instantaneous, reversibility of any change in secondary structure or the general conformation is fully consistent with the above concept. This includes the restoration of all the original characterisitcs, such as the degree of spiralization or the size and shape of the particles, following the complete "melting" of the helices and the thermal unfolding of the chains (Spirin, Gavrilova et al., 1959b; Bogdanova et al., 1962).

It might be added that since RNA in solution has no fixed secondary structure, so that the latter varies freely—and reversibly—as the conditions existing in the solution are altered, the term "denaturing," in the generally accepted sense, does not seem applicable to this structure. This is all the more true because it has not yet been ascertained to what extent the secondary structure studied in solution can be identified as "native"—in other words, how closely this structure approximates to the one existing in the natural, functioning, live systems (see Chapter IV).

Nevertheless, the over-all conclusion to be drawn from the above discussion of the fundamentals relating to the secondary RNA structure is that any RNA molecule, under the particular conditions existing in a given solution, will spontaneously develop a "unique" pattern of secondary structure, determined by the specific nucleotide sequence in the RNA chain. The point was brought up with particular emphasis in the report by Fresco et al. (1960). In fact, an earlier communication by Spirin, Gavrilova et al. (1959b) likewise stressed that the minute (specific) details characterizing the conformation of virus RNA in solution are determined "by the opportunities for coiling and spiralization which depend on the nucleotide sequence as such." From this angle, the possible role of a unique macrostructure in the biologic activity (infectivity) of RNA was discussed in detail, for the particular case of a free RNA from TMV, in a specialized review (Spirin and Gavrilova, 1961).

2. ARRANGEMENT OF HELICAL REGIONS (TERTIARY STRUCTURE)

In some of the reports published by the Doty laboratory (Doty et al., 1959; Boedtker, 1959, 1960) it has been suggested that the RNA molecules possess no tertiary structure. In 1960, however, Dvorkin and Spirin reported new data on UV dichroism noted in the oriented molecules of high-polymeric RNA. Their observations indicate the existence of a specific orientation in the arrangement of chain links within the RNA molecule, which is contrary to the idea of a random arrangement of helical regions.

Studies of the anisotropy exhibited by oriented molecules in the process of light absorption appear to provide the most direct method for determining the orientation of the relevant chromophore groups in these molecules. In the case of nucleic acids, the nitrogenous bases perform the function of the chromophore groups which absorb UV light, the maximum absorption taking place in the neighborhood of 260 mμ.

It is generally known that maximum absorption of plane-polarized UV light by purine and pyrimidine bases is observed in the particular case where the plane in which the base lies coincides with the direction of the electric vector of the light wave. The minimum absorption will be displayed by bases whose planes are oriented at right angles to the direction of the electric vector of light (see review by Beaven et al., 1955). Consider now the case where all the molecules of a nucleic acid are oriented in the same direction. Let the difference in the UV light absorption values be determined for the respective cases where the electric vector of light coincides with, or is at right angles to, the long axes of the molecules.

This will yield a fairly consistent answer as to how the base planes are oriented relative to the long axis of the molecule. With a random orientation, there will be no difference in the absorption of light polarized in mutually perpendicular directions (the molecules will be isotropic, lacking in dichroism of their own). If most base planes are oriented at right angles to the long axis of the molecule, as observed in native DNA, the light absorption by the molecules will be maximum when the electric vector of light is perpendicular to the long axes of the molecules (negative dichroism). The molecules of native DNA, in fact, exhibit strong negative dichroism when oriented in one direction—either in films, by means of stretching, in solution, owing to the flow gradient, or through superposition of an electric field (Thorell and Ruch, 1951; Seeds, 1953; Beaven et al., 1955; Dvorkin, 1960, 1961; Dvorkin and Krinskiy, 1961). If absorption is maximum when the electric vector of light runs parallel to the long axes of molecules (positive dichroism), the planes of the bases must be oriented predominantly in the same direction. The latter case was confirmed in experiments on high-polymeric RNA (virus, ribosomal) in solution (Dvorkin and Spirin, 1960; Bogdanova et al., 1962).

In recent studies conducted by us jointly with G. A. Dvorkin, the orientation of the nitrogenous bases in the RNA particle was determined by a method based on evaluating the absorption of polarized monochromatic light at 260 mμ by oriented molecules (Spirin and Dvorkin, 1960; Bogdanova et al., 1962). The molecule orientation was controlled by superposition of an electric field. The test samples were 0.003-0.02% RNA solutions in phosphate buffer (pH 7.2) varying in ionic strength. Measurements were performed on solutions placed in a Kerr cell, a cuvette made of fused quartz glass with electrode leads inserted into it. Square pulses, duration 1-2 msec, repetition frequency 3-20 cps, were fed to the cell input. The field gradient was varied from 0 to 200 V/cm. Polarized monochromatic light was passed through the cell filled with the test solution and allowed to fall upon a photomultiplier. The photocurrent was recorded by an oscillograph. In the course of experimental work, the dichroic ratio D was determined, i.e., the ratio of optical densities of the solution, obtained, respectively, for mutually perpendicular directions of the electric vector of the light wave—one parallel with, the other at right angles to, the direction of the electric fields. Test preparations included virus RNA from TMV and ribosomal RNA from *E. coli.*

Measurements made on both virus and ribosomal RNA at room temperature showed that when an electric pulse field is superposed on the cell, the polarized UV light becomes modulated on leaving the cell. A graphic presentation of these data is given in Fig. 11. The peak photocurrent strength is shown for the electric pulse duration of about 1 msec. In virus RNA tests the light modulation became apparent when the field gradient equaled 60 V/cm, and was maximum at 120 V/cm. In testing ribosomal RNA somewhat higher field gradients, from 100 to 200 V/cm, were required. This, it seems, could be related without much difficulty to the fact that the virus RNA molecules, having larger dimensions than those of ribosomal RNA, can be more easily oriented by the electric field.

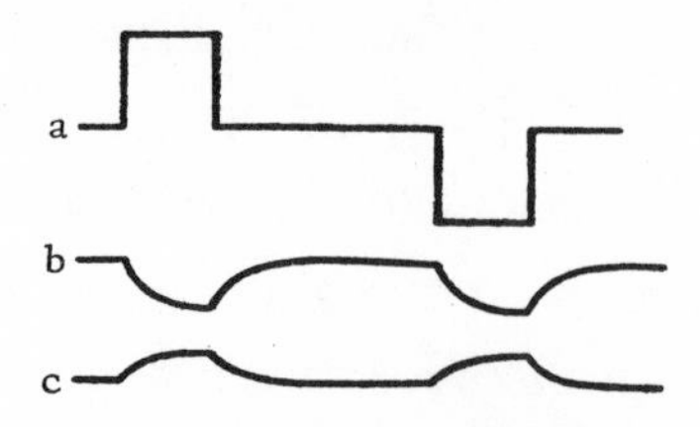

Fig. 11. Respective shapes of electric pulses and photocurrent pulses as functions of the direction of light vector polarization. a—Electric pulses; b—photocurrent pulses, for light polarized in parallel with electric field; c—photocurrent pulses, for light polarized at right angles to electric field (Dvorkin and Spirin, 1960).

The observed modulation of polarized UV light leaving the cell, effected by the superposed electric field, indicates anisotropic absorption of UV light (dichroism) by the oriented molecules of high-polymeric RNA. Evidently, under these conditions, the arrangement of bases in the molecule is not a random one, and the RNA molecule is not a statistically determined coil. This suggests an ordered orientation of the individual links and areas of the chain relative to the particle as a whole. Any arrangement of these links and areas must follow some specific regularity pattern. All of which means that there must be a tertiary structure in existence.*

---

*An ordered arrangement can hardly be due to the superposition of an electric field. Rather, the observed results can be attributed to the orientation of the molecule as a whole, and not of the helical regions in it. This is evident from the following: (a) The observed electrooptical effect is considerable, and approaches saturation at relatively low electric field gradients (120 V/cm for RNA from TMV and 200 V/cm for RNA from *E. coli*). Such moderate gradients are not likely to cause substantial intramolecular changes, but are just high enough for orienting the macromolecules of polyelectrolytes (see O'Konski and Haltner, 1957). (b) Relaxation time values clearly indicate that orientation involves the particle as a whole. (c) According to the most recent experimental data of Dvorkin et al., relaxed behavior is the same as shown for RNA in studies on electrical double refraction, under analogous conditions.

In working with both types of test preparations—virus RNA and ribosomal RNA from *E. coli*—it was found that when the electric vector of the light wave was polarized at right angles to the electric field, the photocurrent became amplified while the pulse was being transmitted, i.e., the light absorption diminished. Conversely, when the electric vector of light was polarized parallel to the electric field, the light absorption increased. It follows that solutions of high-polymeric RNA at room temperature in an electric field display a positive dichroism. Measurements of the dichroic ratio D at room temperature gave a value of 1.2 for RNA solutions of low ionic strength (0.01 and less). Tests of ribosomal RNA from *E. coli* yielded a maximum dichroic ratio value (~+1.2 at 200 V/cm) identical with the corresponding value obtained for virus RNA (+1.2 at 120 V/cm). With an increase in the ionic strength of the solution, the dichroic ratio declined to 1.1, corresponding to the ionic strength of 0.1.

Thus, solutions containing RNA molecules oriented by an electric field and kept at room temperature exhibit a distinct positive dichroism, which is particularly pronounced in preparations of low ionic strength. In RNA particles acted upon by an electric field, the long axes are presumably oriented along the direction of the field. This will be clear if we consider that polyelectrolytes in solution, acted upon by an electric field, become oriented largely because of the polarization and deformation of their ionic atmosphere along the direction of the field. In the particular case of an asymmetrical particle, the direction of this deformation will tend to coincide with that of the long axis (see, for instance, O'Konski and Halter, 1957). It is known, on the other hand, that absorption of polarized light at 260 mμ reaches a maximum when the direction of the electric vector of light coincides with the plane of the nitrogenous base in the molecule. It is concluded that under the conditions as discussed, the bases of an RNA molecule are oriented predominantly parallel to the long axis of the molecule. We might add that DNA, in which the bases are oriented at right angles to the long axis of the molecule, displays a negative dichroism.

We have described the structural transformation observed in heated RNA solutions, which involves a rupture of the hydrogen bonds inside the molecule, followed by the unfolding of a polynucleotide chain within a definite temperature range. The RNA macromolecules change from one configuration to another—from a state of compact particle to a loose unfolded state of the polynucleotide chain. The changes in RNA configuration taking place on heating must entail changes in the orientation of the bases relative to one another, within the molecule. Considering these relationships, we found it necessary to follow up the variation of the dichroic ratio with the temperature of an RNA solution.

To this end, measurements were performed in a cell provided with a thermostat (Dvorkin and Spirin, 1960). When a solution of virus RNA buffered with phosphate, ionic strength 0.01, was heated from 10 to 30° C, the dichroic ratio remained positive and constant ($D = +1.2$). At 40° C, the dichroic ratio equaled unity ($D = 1$). At 50° C, dichroism changes its sign, i.e., became negative ($D =$ 1.1) (Fig. 12, curve 1). The effect was found to be reversible, since a positive dichroism was re-established on cooling ($D =$ 1.2 at 20° C). In solutions having an ionic strength of 0.1, the effect remained qualitatively the same but changed quantitatively. The amplitude of the photocurrent pulse and the magnitude of the dichroic ratio both decreased (see Fig. 12, curve 2). Fully consistent with the above results were the data obtained for ribosomal RNA from *E. coli* on heating under comparable conditions (Bogdanova et al., 1962).

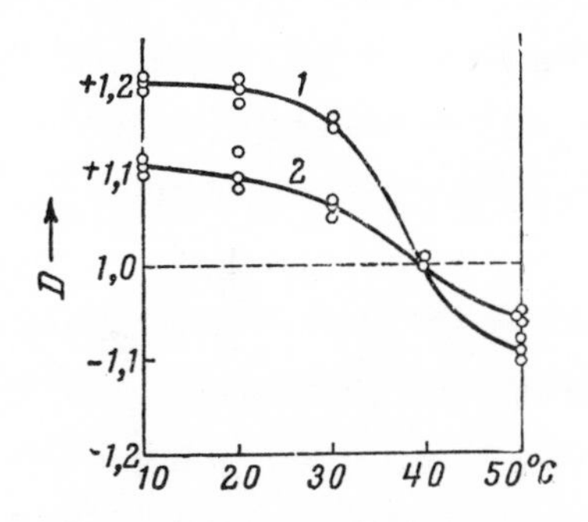

Fig. 12. Variation of dichroic ratio D in heated solutions of virus RNA differing in ionic strength. 1—Solutions with ionic strength less than or equal to 0.01; 2—solutions with ionic strength of 0.1 (Dvorkin and Spirin, 1960).

The change in dichroism sign from positive to negative, in the course of heating the solution, signifies that at elevated temperatures the nitrogenous bases become oriented predominantly at right angles to the long axis of the molecule. Inasmuch as the bases are invariably oriented at right angles to the direction of the phosphodiester links in the chain, it follows that the orientation of bases perpendicular to the long axis of the particle as a unit must be taken as a sign of disintegration of the helical regions, with the RNA chain uncoiled and straightened out lengthwise. It was shown earlier, in fact, that as the temperature rises, the polynucleotide chain is gradually straightened out and the helical regions diminish in number, i.e., a transition to an unfolded configuration takes place.

To evaluate any possible causal relationship between the electrooptical effects as described and the high-polymeric state of RNA, control experiments were set up, in which crystalline ribonuclease was added to the tested solution (Dvorkin and Spirin, 1960). The effect of treatment was to eliminate, practically within seconds, the light modulation.

The above data not only establish an ordered structure for the macromolecules of RNA in solution but are perhaps descriptive of the actual nature of such orientation. Over the temperature range of 10-30° C the RNA solution exhibited a positive dichroism, indicating, as stated above, that the planes wherein the rings of the bases lie were predominantly parallel to the long axis of the molecule. In the light of available data on the RNA secondary structure, with its double-stranded helical regions, the latter can be visualized as oriented at right angles to the long axis of the particle. In this case, the plane orientation for the nitrogenous bases will, as a matter of fact, be parallel to the axis of the particle, in perfect agreement with the RNA dichroism data. A schematic presentation of a tertiary structure for RNA molecules in a solution of moderate ionic strength, which was offered by us in 1960, is not as consistent with the above data (Spirin, 1960; see also Spirin and Gavrilova, 1961; Bogdanova et al., 1962). The recent experiments by Frisman et al. (1963) on the double refraction of high-polymeric RNA, in a low-gradient flow of solution, are also interpreted by the authors as consistent with the above model structure. Two possible variants of the actual orientation of helices, in accordance with the proposed concepts of the tertiary structure, are shown schematically in Fig. 13. As we examine the diagram, we must keep in mind that it preassigns no fixed position for any helical region relative to other such neighboring areas. The only point emphasized in the diagram is that the helical regions are oriented at right angles to the long axis of the particle. In the plane perpendicular to this long axis, the axes of the various helical regions appear to be oriented at random, along different directions which are most likely distributed statistically over 360°, about the same long axis of the particle.

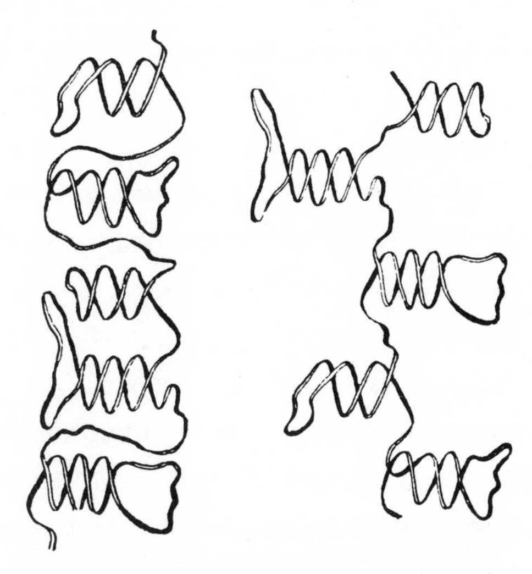

Fig. 13. The probable tertiary structure of RNA; the helical regions are oriented at right angles to the long axis of the particle (fragment). Two possible variants are shown (Spirin, 1960, 1962; Bogdanova et al., 1962).

Such orientation of the helical areas in the RNA molecule imposes some specific additional requirements that the structural organization must satisfy. Two important conclusions follow regarding the conformation of RNA in solution. The helical regions incorporated in the structure of a particle such as shown in the diagram (Fig. 13) must form basically as a result of interaction of individual pairs involving adjacent (neighboring) areas in a single-stranded polynucleotide chain. Fresco, Alberts and Doty, starting from different premises, reached the same conclusion, namely, that ". . .the most stable helical regions arise from interaction between adjacent sections of the polynucelotide backbone. . . . Entropy considerations suggest that interactions between distant sections are unlikely, since they would lead to very highly restrictive conformations. Thus, the helical regions take the form of hairpin turns which require a minimum of three unbonded nucleotides to connect the antiparallel hydrogen-bonded chain section." If we apply this proposition, unqualified, to high-polymeric RNA containing a large number of helical regions and if some electrostatic repulsion is assumed to act between these areas, we shall arrive, by an independent route, at one of the structural schemes describing the arrangement of helices (Fig. 13).

The second important conclusion concerns the arrangement of helical regions, which are seen in the diagram to be "stacked up in a row." This type of consecutive buildup will tend to impart a rod-shaped conformation to the particle as a whole, assuming a sufficient number of helical structures to be present (as is the case with high-polymeric RNA). In solutions of moderate ionic strength, electrostatic repulsion is still sufficiently distinct. Under these conditions, the numerous helical hairpin-shaped loops (helical regions) protruding in all directions from the long axis (see Fig. 13, especially the right-hand variant) will display mutual repulsion along the entire length of the particle. This will create a tendency toward an orientation in planes parallel to one another, so that the particle as a whole will tend to take the form of a rod in a state of electrostatic tension. Such a structure will thus be supported solely by forces of electrostatic repulsion, given a covalent framework linking the individual helical regions consecutively. If we recognize the important function of complex metallic bridges and nonspecific hydrogen bonds in the RNA macromolecule, a possibility will suggest itself that the neighboring helical regions may be connected in some way to form such structures as shown in the left-hand variant (Fig. 13). It has in fact been confirmed by numerous independent experimental studies that the molecules of high-polymeric RNA, when in solutions of moderate ionic strength, assume a rod-shaped configuration (see Chapter III, 3).

To sum up the data on the fundamental tertiary structure of high-polymeric RNA in solutions of moderate ionic strength at room temperature, we can state that short "hairpin-shaped," double-stranded helical areas are oriented predominantly at right angles to the long axis of the RNA molecule as a whole, and that such regions alternate with nonspiralized single-stranded areas. The arrangement in which the "stacked-up" helical regions alternate with disoriented areas results in forming a rod-shaped particle.

Characteristically, no oriented diffraction pictures were ever obtained for high-polymeric RNA (Zubay and Wilkins, 1960; Klug et al., 1961), while some degree of orientation was established for low-polymeric preparations of "soluble" RNA (Brown and Zubay, 1960) and for what appears to have been fairly degraded RNA in the early experiments of Rich and Watson (1954a, b). An explanation will be found in the proposed schematic presentation of the tertiary structure (Fig. 13). It can be seen from these diagrams that in the case of high-polymeric RNA, even if the particles have been successfully oriented, there will be no distinct orientation of the helix axes in any one direction. A partial orientation seems possible, however, in working with degraded RNA, whose structure shows the presence of quasi-independent, separate short helices or fragments comprising 2-3 helical regions, linked by a flexible nonspiralized area. For the same reason, apparently, it is possible to attain a partial orientation of the helix axes in the case of "soluble" RNA. It is immaterial whether this acid is visualized structurally as a single double-stranded helix (Brown and Zubay, 1960) or in the form of three short helical regions linked by nonspiralized areas (Fresco et al., 1960). This is shown in Fig. 14. The above interpretation is confirmed by the most recent experiments of Frisman and co-workers (1963). According to these authors, the positive double refraction in the flow of solution noted for high-polymeric RNA was seen to change to negative double refraction after partial degradation of the same acid. In the latter case, the experimenters pointed out, the DNA-like helices had their long axes oriented along the direction of the flow.

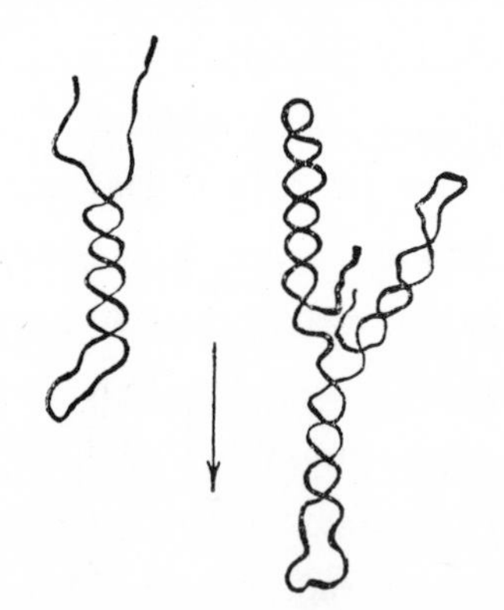

Fig. 14. The most probable orientation of short fragments in high-polymeric RNA, or of molecules in "soluble" RNA, in solution flow or in a film when stretched.

It will be noted, however, that such a helix orientation with respect to the long axis of the molecule, as shown in Fig. 13, and the rod-shaped molecule conformation in high-polymeric RNA appear to be characteristic only of solutions whose ionic strength is not high.

With an increase in ionic strength, the repulsion between the helices diminishes and the particles tend to coil some more, with the resulting disorientation of the helical structures. If that is the case, then the appearance of helical structures in solutions of high ionic strength can be attributed to "supercoiling" of the extended, rod-shaped molecule under consideration, rather than to the coiling of a single-stranded polynucleotide chain as a whole. The original tertiary structure is basically preserved, but it is now complicated by additional coiled cross-linkages, with many turns and twists. This concept—in which coils formed after an increase in ionic strength are envisioned as tightly wound-up rods—is consistent with the view held by Fresco and co-workers (Fresco et al., 1960), who contend that the maximum stability of a conformation is attained primarily through the interaction between adjacent chain sections (hairpin-shaped helical regions).

A point to be stressed is that the proposed basic arrangement of the helical regions, as envisaged above, applies almost solely to the molecule of high-polymeric RNA. The existence of any regularity pattern in the orientation of helical areas can scarcely be assumed for "soluble" RNA. If the molecule of "soluble" RNA is taken to be constituted as a chain which forms a single helix by folding upon itself (making U-turns: Brown and Zubay, 1960; see Chapter III, 3b, Fig. 9), then a tertiary structure seems out of the question. If, on the other hand, this molecule is visualized as forming several (say, three) helical regions (Fresco et al., 1960; see Fig. 10), then lack of an ordered arrangement will appear more plausible. In solutions of low ionic strength, the electrostatic repulsion acting between the helical region may apparently result in a "stellar" arrangement (Chapter III, 3b).

3. MOLECULAR SHAPES AND TRANSITIONAL CONFIGURATIONS

a) High-Polymeric RNA

As mentioned earlier, all high-polymeric RNA, when in solution at moderate temperatures and in the presence of at least a small amount of salts, occurs as highly compact, compressed (tightly coiled) particles. The possible shape of such particles has been discussed since the first experiments on the isolation of high-polymeric RNA were undertaken. The matter is closely associated with the concept of the tertiary structure for RNA in solution. The absence of a tertiary structure means a random, statistically determined arrangement of the chain links within the particle; hence, the molecule must take the form of a statistically determined coil. The presence of a tertiary structure implies some kind of chain arrangement other than a random one, and such an ordered structure may be reflected in the shape of the molecule.

By studying the asymmetry of light scattering at various wavelengths, Hopkins and Sinsheimer (1955) obtained early evidence of a structure patterned to meet the requirements of a rod-shaped model for the molecules of virus RNA in solutions of low ionic strength. Calculations based on such dispersion data yielded consistently the same value only for an RNA molecule assumed to have a rod-shaped conformation. The average length of such a particle was estimated as equal to 1600 Å. It was further shown in the same study that the length and, apparently, the shape of the particles depend on the ionic strength of solution. On addition of salts, the length diminishes and the particles possibly assume a less asymmetric configuration.

Timashev and co-workers carried out a detailed study on high-polymeric RNA of animal origin (ascites cancer of Ehrlich), using basically the same light-scattering procedure as described above. The conclusion they reached was that the most satisfactory model of RNA molecules in solution, even for ionic strength of 0.1, is an elongated spheroid or a rod (Timashev et al., 1958; Kronman et al., 1960). In the first of these reports, the rods were described as ranging from 41-51 Å in diameter and 700-1000 Å in length, as calculated from light dispersion data. Some unpublished electron microscope data of Brown, cited by the authors, confirm the rod-shaped configuration of the particles. The latter, while varying in length, were found by Brown to have about the same length, 40-45 Å.

In earlier experiments using an electron microscope, Hart (1955, 1958) examined TMV particles, partially deproteinized at one end by a detergent, as well as particles of virus RNA deposited upon a substrate film in the form of an aqueous solution. The experimenter observed "fibrils" of RNA about 40 Å in diameter; in other words, he too appears to have discovered the rod-shaped form of high-polymeric RNA. Rod-shaped particles measuring about 30 Å in diameter were seen to predominate also in the electron microphotographs obtained by Hall (1959) for RNA from calf's liver.

Finally, in studies on UV dichroism displayed by the molecules of high-polymeric RNA, the latter were shown to be capable of being readily oriented in an electric field with a gradient as low as about 100 V/cm. This was demonstrated for RNA of both virus (Dvorkin and Spirin, 1960) and ribosomal origin (Bogdanova et al., 1962), in solutions of relatively low ionic strength, 0.01 and less. The observed facts indicate, most likely, some considerable asymmetry in the RNA macromolecules. The same experiments showed these molecules to have a highly ordered conformation (tertiary structure; see Chapter III, 2) under such conditions as described. The latter observation, apart from the other data, led to the conclusion that the molecules of high-polymeric RNA in solutions of moderate ionic strength are probably constituted as rod-shaped particles rather than as disoriented, statistically determined coils.

At the same time, as mentioned earlier, communications released by the Doty laboratory brought forth extensive evidence that the molecules of high-polymeric RNA possess no tertiary structure, but are randomly coiled, statistically coiled structures possessing some degree of spatial asymmetry, varying with the ionic strength of solution (Hall and Doty, 1958, 1959; Boedtker, 1959, 1960). The authors' calculations were based primarily on an RNA molecule conceived of as such a coil. The selected model, moreover, proved correct, as evidenced by the agreement of results obtained by different physicochemical measurement techniques (basically, light-scattering data contrasted with viscosity and sedimentation).

Most painstaking were the considerations offered by Boedtker (1960), who argued for the randomly coiled, tangled particle concept relating to high-polymeric RNA. His evidence rested on three basic groups of observations: (a) calculation of rotation radius for RNA molecules, either from light-scattering data or by use of the Flori-Fox equation for randomly coiled polymers, yielded respective values which were in complete agreement; (b) the ratio of molecular weight to rotation radius squared, computed from the light-scattering data, remained fairly constant as the molecular weight diminished owing to slow degradation, which was consistent with the anticipated behavior of a nonoriented tangled structure; some slight decline in the ratio value in the course of degradation could be accounted for by an increase in the polydispersity of the particles; (c) the relationship between the sedimentation coefficient and molecular weight obeyed the equation derived for a nonoriented, compressed, tangled structure: $M = K \times S^2$. It was concluded that the RNA molecule is a nonoriented coil, with statistically distributed, short helical regions (Boedtker, 1960). However, on examining the factual material cited by Boedtker as proof of a coiled RNA configuration, it becomes evident that her measurements, both hydrodynamic (viscosity and sedimentation) and optical (light scattering), were carried out in a phosphate buffer, the ionic strength approximating 0.2. It seems highly probable that given such a high ionic strength, the molecular structure observed by Boedtker was indeed a coil constituting the RNA particle.

Dvorkin and Spirin (1960) believed that with an increase in the ionic strength of solution the RNA molecule changes its form from the rod-shaped to a more distinctly ball-shaped pattern. The assumption was based on measurements of UV dichroism under the influence of an electric field (the dichroism decreased while the extent of spiralization increased). Such behavior is consistent with the early data of Hopkins and Sinsheimer (1955) on light scattering by virus RNA (see above) and with later observations reported by Littauer and Eisenberg (1959). According to these authors, double refraction by a flow of ribosomal

RNA was eliminated when the ionic strength of solution was increased to 0.2. Electron microscope studies by the Littauer team (Littauer et al., 1960; Dannon et al., 1961) disclosed an aggregation of molecules in solutions of ribosomal RNA of relatively high ionic strength (0.1 *M* ammonium acetate) deposited on a film. In many areas, typical coiled particles could be discerned.

From these data it may be concluded that the shape of RNA molecules, in solutions kept at room temperature, is determined by the ionic strength of the solution. When it is relatively low, ranging approximately from 10^{-2} to 10^{-3} or 10^{-4}, the molecules of high-polymeric RNA may be said to have a rod-shaped conformation. When the ionic strength is comparatively high—0.1-0.2 and higher—the RNA molecules tend to become coiled. Such structural patterns may result from a more or less random coiling of the preexisting elongated rods (see Chapter III, 2a).

As stated earlier, on heating the solution the compact RNA conformations become disrupted and the chain changes over to an unfolded state, losing its tertiary and secondary structures in the process. The existence of such transition was brought to light in studies of hydrodynamic properties displayed by virus RNA on heating (Gavrilova et al., 1959; Spirin, Gavrilova et al., 1959b) and was confirmed by data on UV dichroism in heated RNA solutions (Dvorkin and Spirin, 1960). An identical picture of thermal unfolding was demonstrated by the same techniques (viscosity, sedimentation, UV dichroism) for ribosomal RNA of various origins (Spirin and Mil'man, 1960; Spirin, 1961a; Bogdanova et al., 1962). Thus RNA, when heated, assumes a new configuration, identifiable as an unfolded, single-thread, polynucleotide chain.

Laboratory studies of ribosomal RNA (Cox and Littauer, 1959) and virus RNA (report by Haschemeyer et al., of the Fraenkel-Conrat laboratory, in 1959) demonstrated a similar transition from a compact to an unfolded state for RNA transferred to salt-free aqueous solutions. Littauer and co-workers confirmed this with the aid of an electron microscope on various RNA samples (Littauer et al., 1960; Dannon et al., 1961).

A transition caused by heating, or by reducing the ionic strength to the lowest possible value, was found to be reversible in all cases. Thermal transition was observed in solutions of both low (rod—unfolded fibril) and high (coiled structure—unfolded fibril) ionic strength.

On the basis of the then available data, a proposition was advanced by us in 1960, asserting the existence of three extreme, mutually reversible types of conformation in high-polymeric RNA (Spirin, 1960).

The proposition rests on the fact that the conformation of RNA in solution is fully determined and controlled by an equilibrium resulting from a free and reversible interplay of intramolecular forces—notably, the interaction between the hydrogen bonds and the forces of electrostatic repulsion. The RNA molecule is thought to embody all such molecular forces at equilibrium, as a balanced structure, which is not fixed by any cross-linking but is determined solely by the relationship of forces existing under any given specific conditions. It is precisely this balancing of mutually opposing forces that is believed to determine the degree of chain coiling, spatial asymmetry and compactness of the particle. At some specific level of salt concentration in the solution, the negatively charged phosphate groups become sufficiently screened. The forces of hydrogen bonding will then considerably exceed such electrostatic repulsion as exists under these conditions. The result is a compact conformation abounding in helical regions. An increase in the ionic strength leads to a more extensive screening of the phosphate groups, with further decline in electrostatic repulsion within the macromolecule. The hydrogen bonds increase in number and the particle becomes increasingly coiled. A decrease in ionic strength has the opposite effect, causing the chain to unfold to a point where it is completely uncoiled. This means that the electrostatic repulsion now exceeds the intramolecular forces of hydrogen bonding, and is able to cause rupture of the hydrogen bonds. The chain is straightened out, with some tension created along its length. Addition of urea, formamide, or dimethyl sulfoxide results in a weakening of the intramolecular hydrogen bonds along with any hydrophobic interaction. The same effect of loosening the macromolecular structure is thus achieved in yet another way, and the chain unfolding is further enhanced.

Heating the solution leads to a thermal rupture of the hydrogen bonds, and the chain is again unfolded, forming a rather loose structure. A clearly defined RNA conformation is attained only when the chain links interact freely and reversibly, until a state has been reached which is most effective in terms of the stability and the energy level, under the given conditions. When the conditions are altered, the structure undergoes some adaptive changes. If the original conditions are restored, the former structure re-emerges.

The RNA macromolecules are thus seen to vary in conformation depending on such conditions as the ionic strength, temperature, and other parameters.

In solutions of low ionic strength kept at room temperature, these molecules take the form of rods made up of short, ordered helical regions alternating with disoriented areas. With an increase in ionic strength, the structural asymmetry becomes less pronounced as the rods change over to a fairly compact coiled configuration. A temperature rise causes a transition of the macromolecular structure to a state in which the molecules appear as somewhat straightened fibrils or loosened, disoriented coiled patterns. All such extreme conformations are interrelated through reversible transitional patterns. A schematic presentation of these concepts is given in Fig. 15.

In a study undertaken by us jointly with N. A. Kiselev and L. P. Gavrilova, we attempted to verify the proposed structural configurations. For this purpose, shape and size variations in RNA macromolecules with altered conditions were followed up, using a direct visual method based on electron microscope observations (Kiselev, Gavrilova and Spirin, 1960a, b). Test preparations included both infectious RNA from TMV and ribosomal RNA from *E. coli*. In preparing samples for electron microscopy, the following modifications of solutions were used: (a) an RNA solution in an ammonium acetate buffer of relatively low ionic strength, 0.0003 to 0.001, kept at room temperature; (b) a buffered RNA solution of relatively high ionic strength, up to 0.15, at room temperature; (c) an RNA solution heated to 70° C; (d) an RNA solution acidified with acetic acid, at room temperature. The test solution was deposited on mica and dried, and the particles were preshadowed with a platinum-palladium alloy at an appropriate angle so as to obtain a ratio of object height to shadow length ranging from 1:7 to 1:10. The carbon replica method was used to prepare preshadowed samples. By varying

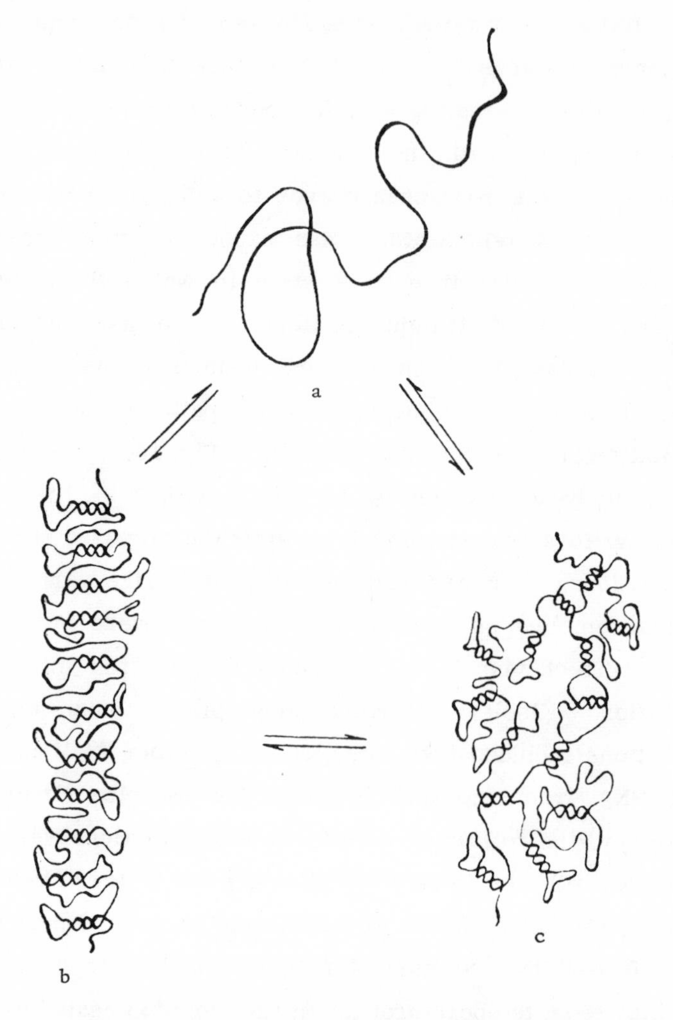

Fig. 15. Conformations and transitional configurations proposed for macromolecules of high-polymeric RNA in solution, as dependent on ionic strength, temperature and pH (coiled pattern—rod—unfolded fibril). Schematic presentation (Spirin and Gavrilova, 1961).

the ionic strength and temperature of test solutions, we were able to observe under the electron microscope all three extreme RNA configurations as anticipated: rod-, coil-, and fibril-shaped.

In test solutions of low ionic strength, at room temperature (variant 1), both virus and ribosomal RNA particles actually resembled rods. A general view of rod-shaped virus RNA molecules, as they appeared in the field of vision of the electron microscope, at relatively low magnification, is shown in Fig. 16. Individual rod-shaped particles of virus and ribosomal RNA are seen at higher magnification in Figs. 17 and 18. In both cases the height of a horizontally placed rod (its diameter), as calculated from the length of its shadow, ranges from 26-31 Å. The rods of virus and ribosomal RNA are practically indistinguishable, in terms of their characteristic general appearance, except that the former are longer than the latter. Virus RNA rods reach a maximum length of 2500 Å. Calculating the rod volume as a product—$26 \times 31 \times 250$ $Å^3$—we obtain a value approximating 2×10^6 $Å^3$, which corresponds to the volume of a virus RNA particle having a molecular weight of 2×10^6. The maximum length, for ribosomal RNA rods, is about 1000-1200 Å. Consequently, their volume equals approximately 1×10^6 $Å^3$, which is in fair agreement with the molecular volume of the large component in ribosomal RNA. However, the maximum mean distribution length amounts to 600 Å. When used in volume computations, this value, characteristic for the predominant type of particles, gives a volume of about 5×10^5 $Å^3$, which appears to correspond to the small component in ribosomal RNA. The rod-shaped molecular conformation, in solutions of low ionic strength, at room temperature, fully agrees with the idea of transitions from one configuration to another affecting RNA macromolecules in solution. The observed phenomenon is consistent also with the assumption that such macromolecules assume, under specific conditions, a rod-shaped conformation. Moreover, the dimensions obtained for rod-shaped particles

Fig. 16. Electron microphotograph showing particles of high-polymeric RNA from a solution having an ionic strength of 0.0003 ("rods"). Ratio of object height to shadow length is 1:10. Magnification 50,000 (photo by N. A. Kiselev).

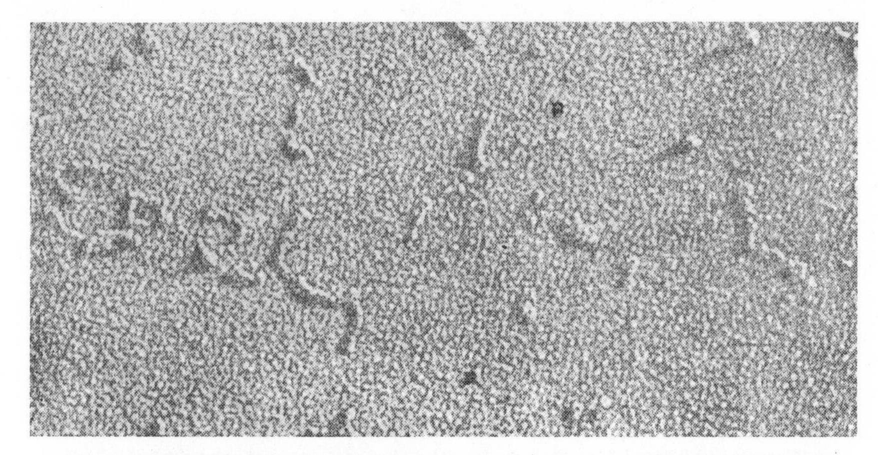

Fig. 17. Electron microphotograph showing particles of virus (TMV) from a solution having an ionic strength of 0.0003 ("rods"). Ratio of object height to shadow length is 1:9.0. Magnification 100,000 (Kiselev et al., 1961b).

Fig. 18. Electron microphotograph showing particles of ribosomal (*E. coli*) RNA from a solution having an ionic strength of 0.0003 ("rods"). Ratio of object height to shadow length is 1:10. Magnification 100,000 (Kiselev et al., 1961b).

(height, 25–31 Å) agree well with the proposed schematic representation of a tertiary structure, envisaged for the rod-shaped RNA macromolecules (see Fig. 13). In the diagram, the short, double-stranded helical regions in high-polymeric RNA are shown to be oriented predominantly at right angles to the long axis of the particle. These areas are linked successively, forming a rod-shaped structure. When deposited upon a supporting film for replica impressions, the height of such rods will be indicated in some spots along the substrate by the diameters of the double polyribonucleotide helices (where the latter happen to lie flat on the support) and in other spots possibly by the length of the helical regions (wherever these are standing upright on the film). The diameter of a double-stranded helix consisting of polyribonucleotides of the AU-complex type, when in a dry state, is known to equal about 25 Å. The length of one full turn of such a double helix approximates 30 Å. It follows that experimentally obtained values for the height of rod-shaped particles are close to the characteristic dimensions of the RNA molecule consisting of "stacked-up" short, double-stranded helical regions having an average length equal to about one full turn of the helix.

In examining the tertiary structure of rod-shaped RNA particles, it is assumed, as a basic premise, that the short, double-stranded helical regions are formed as a result of interaction and mutual spiralization of adjacent areas in a single-stranded polynucleotide chain. Such a formation process has been established by electron microscope examination for rod-shaped particles in test solutions of low ionic strength (see Fig. 19). Here, the compact rod-shaped configuration is seen to be distended, forming a fairly loose structure. In the elongated RNA molecules (Fig. 19), extremely thin areas can be discerned—evidently portions of a single-stranded polynucleotide fibril—alternating with considerably thicker "nodal" spots, indicating double-stranded helical regions, formed by a single-stranded polynucleotide as it bends upon itself (U-turn). On heating the solution a few isolated double-stranded helical regions, still intact, can be discerned in the elongated configurations; these become further distended, assuming the shape of strands.

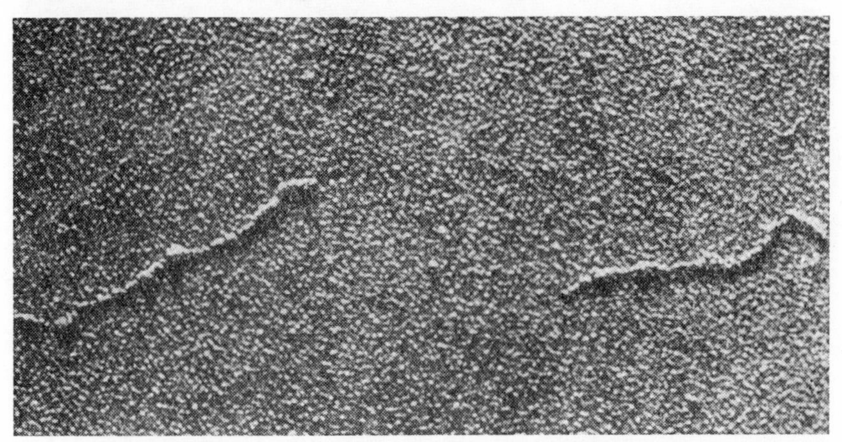

Fig. 19. Electron microphotograph showing particles of virus RNA from a solution having an ionic strength of 0.0001 ("stretched rods"). Ratio of object height to shadow length is 1:9.0. Magnification 120,000 (Kiselev et al., 1961b).

The electron microphotographs of virus RNA, in cases where solutions of high ionic strength, at room temperature, were used in preparing the sample (variant 2), showed flattened, tangled particles, most of them measuring about 400 Å in diameter (Fig. 20). The height of the basic type of such a coiled structure, calculated from the length of the shadow, amounts to 25-32 Å. The particles, identifiable as oblate tangled formations deposited horizontally on the supporting film, have a volume of about 2×10^6 $Å^3$, which is close to the volume of an RNA particle having a molecular weight of 2×10^6, i.e., the molecular weight of virus

Fig. 20. Electron microphotograph showing particles of virus RNA from a solution having an ionic strength of 0.1 ("coils"). Ratio of object height to shadow length is 1:7.6. Magnification 100,000 (Kiselev et al., 1961a, b).

RNA. Examination of microphotographs obtained under identical conditions for ribosomal RNA from *E. coli*, reveals the same type of coiled particles (Fig. 21) as shown for virus RNA in solutions of high ionic strength (variant 2). The particles in Fig. 21 are, however, substantially smaller than those of virus RNA. The predominant type of such coiled particles measures about 200 Å in diameter and 25–30 Å in height, which corresponds to a particle volume of 5×10^5 Å^3. Another, slightly larger type of coil has a diameter of 250–300 Å and the same height equaling 25–30 Å. This corresponds to a particle volume approximating 1.0×10^6 Å^3. The two types of tangled coils, with respective volumes of 5×10^5 Å^3 and 1.0×10^6 Å^3, can apparently be identified with the two high-polymeric components of ribosomal RNA.

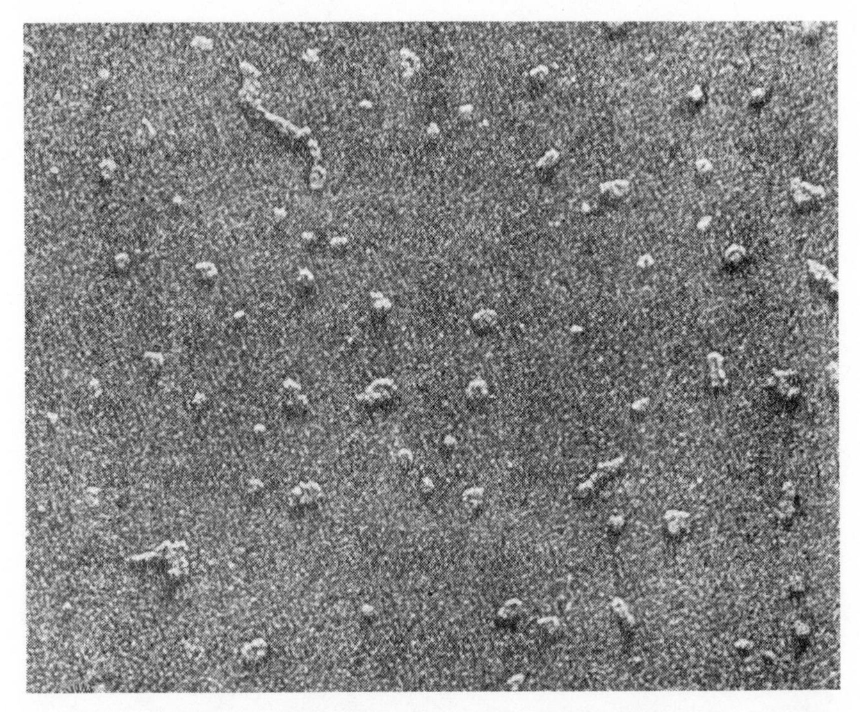

Fig. 21. Electron microphotograph showing particles of ribosomal RNA (*E. coli*) from a solution having an ionic strength of 0.15 ("coils"). Ratio of object height to shadow length is 1:8.5. Magnification 100,000 (Kiselev et al., 1961b).

It was shown earlier that in a heated solution, the molecules of high-polymeric RNA unfold, passing over from the state of a compact particle to a state of a straightened, single-stranded fibril. This was fully confirmed by electron microscopy applied to RNA samples from solutions preheated to 70° C (variant 3). The RNA molecule, in this case, is observed in the form of a thin, very long strand, about 7 Å in height, corresponding to a single-stranded polynucleotide chain (Fig. 22). Single-stranded, unfolded strands of the same type can be seen also in RNA from an acidified solution (Fig. 23). The electron microphotographs of unfolded fibrils verify completely the proposed concept of transitional configurations and, furthermore, confirm the continuity of a polynucleotide chain in the molecule of high-polymeric RNA, both virus and ribosomal.

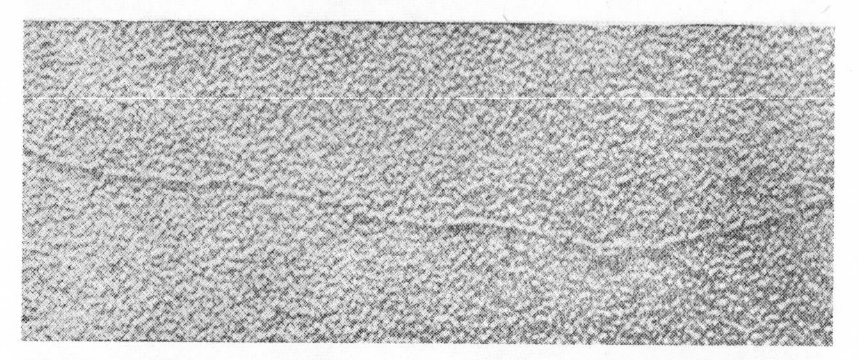

Fig. 22. Electron microphotograph showing a strand of virus RNA from a heated solution (70°C). Ratio of object height to shadow length is 1:9.6. Magnification 87,000 (Kiselev et al., 1961a, b).

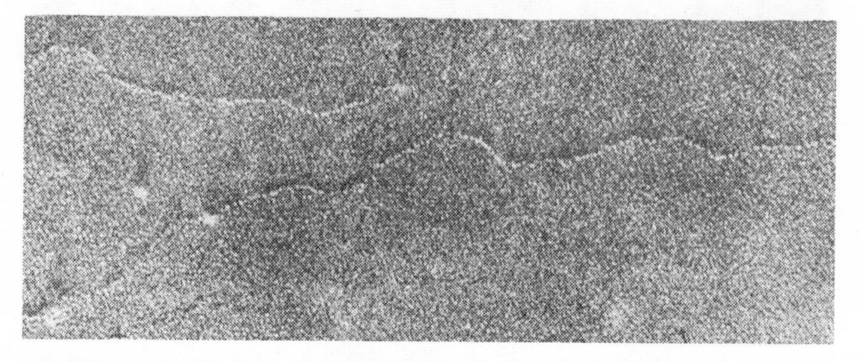

Fig. 23. Electron microphotograph showing a strand of ribosomal RNA (E. coli) from an acidified solution. Ratio of object height to shadow length is 1:10. Magnification 87,000 (Kiselev et al., 1961b).

The sum total of such electron microscope data makes evident the existence of three extreme types of conformations assumed for high-polymeric RNA, along with the proposed transition "coiled particle—rod—strand" (see Fig. 15) based on hydrodynamic and optical measurements carried out on RNA solutions under varying conditions.

In concluding this section, it should be pointed out that in all manifestations of electrostatic forces, in the mechanism supporting the helices, and in the process of stabilizing the entire compact structure of an RNA conformation, a significant role is played by the metal cations bound with the RNA. This refers particularly to the alkaline earths, above all to magnesium, as well as to such transition metals as iron, nickel, etc. The presence of firmly bound metals was reported by Loring and co-workers (Loring and Waritz, 1957; Loring et al., 1958) and later by Wacker and Valley (1959). Haschemeyer and co-workers (1959) pointed out that traces of bivalent cations present in preparations of virus RNA are sufficient for supporting an ordered, coiled conformation of this acid in water free of other ions. The same authors, and also Boedtker (1960), showed that bivalent cations, even in very low concentrations, affect the stability and number of helical regions in RNA to an extent comparable to the effect of univalent ions in a large concentration. Boedtker (1960) described in detail the strong stabilizing influence of magnesium ions as an aid in supporting the helical areas. Fuwa and co-workers (1960) made a special study of transition metals as a factor influencing the RNA structure. The authors concluded that such metals, being firmly bonded with the RNA, stabilize the helical regions, form metal-containing complexes which act as bridges, and thus participate to a large extent in the formation of the tertiary structure in high-polymeric RNA.

b) "Soluble" RNA

"Soluble" RNA, as any other RNA, exists in buffered solutions at room temperature in the form of compact particles. The latter are formed as the single-stranded polynucleotide chain folds upon itself, making a U-turn, and thus undergoes spiralization. The shape of these particles is directly related to the actual mechanism of chain spiralization in "soluble" RNA. A chain consisting of 90 nucleotides, as it is twisted, may be expected to form three helical regions, each having an average length equal to about one full turn of a helix (Fresco et al., 1960). A relevant diagram is shown in Fig. 10. In this case, as mentioned earlier (see Chapter III, 2b), the helical regions will be distributed more or less at random, but their axes will tend toward a radial (stellar) orientation, due to electrostatic repulsion. Considering, however, the relatively moderate length of the polynucleotide chain, we must reckon with the possibility that a single, imperfect helix (a helix with loops) may be formed as the chain folds in half (Fresco et al., 1960) (see Fig. 9). Precisely this kind of model for "soluble" RNA was proposed by Brown and Zubay (1960), based on their experimental data. The author believes the native secondary structure of "soluble" RNA's to be accurately depicted by their scheme, even though they demonstrated that the ability to function as an amino acid acceptor is not dependent on the integrity of this structure.

It should be emphasized that available data provide no basis for singling out one of the two possible molecular shapes of "soluble" RNA as the more plausible.

The compact particles, even when revealed in electron microscope studies of "soluble" RNA (Dannon et al., 1961; Kiselev and Kiselev, 1961), are too fine to permit correct evaluation of their shape and configuration. N. A. Kiselev and L. L. Kiselev, in their report (1961), described rod-shaped particles, but such conformation can be interpreted in many ways. The length of the particles, as reported by these authors, averaged about 80–120 Å, and the height, computed from the length of shadow, approximated 20–25 Å.

As in the case of high-polymeric RNA, heating the solution or decreasing its ionic strength causes an unfolding of the chain in "soluble" RNA, indicated by a hyperchromic effect, diminished optical rotation, and an increase in specific viscosity (Tissieres, 1959; Cox and Littauer, 1960; Littauer, 1960; Brown and Zubay, 1960; Kiselev et al., 1962a, b). Thus, under some specific conditions, soluble RNA, like high-polymeric RNA, will change its configuration, taking the form of an unfolded chain. The transition "compact particle—straightened strand" is completely reversible.

Chapter IV

CONFORMATION OF RNA CHAINS IN RIBOSOMES

In studying the structure of RNA when isolated and present in a free state in solution, a point of major interest involves the way in which the observed structural conformation is related to the biologic functions of the molecules and to the native structure possessed by this acid in living, functioning systems.

"Soluble" RNA has been reported (Tissieres, 1959) to exist in cells largely in a free state. Consequently, it was argued, the chain conformation noted for this acid, when in solution, must remain intact also inside the cell. Ample experimental evidence indicates, moreover, that the various changes which this conformation undergoes in vitro do not in any way affect the functioning of the acid as a carrier of amino acids. From this it was concluded (Brown and Zubay, 1960) that in terms of biological activity it matters little, if at all, whether the secondary structure of "soluble" RNA remains intact. Such considerations are, however, not fully convincing, since they do not allow for the possibility of any reversible changes affecting the same RNA conformation. More particularly, they do not take into account the fact that this acid is capable of assuming a clearly defined, specific configuration under such fairly constant conditions as exist in the protein-synthesizing systems. The change, furthermore, is not related to the conformation possessed by this RNA in solution, previous to its introduction into such a system.

The matter is further complicated in the case of ribosomal RNA, which does not exist independently in the cell but is combined in a certain way with protein to form specific ribonucleoprotein particles. The principal question concerning ribosomal RNA is what type of structure is possessed by high-polymeric RNA present in the ribosomal particle and, furthermore, to what extent the distinctive, fundamental molecular organization of free RNA in solution, as described above, applies to the same RNA as a ribosomal component. The scant data currently available on RNA in ribosomes will be discussed in the sections which follow.

1. HELICAL REGIONS

In the light of such information as is now available, the nature of the helical areas and the extent of spiralization appear to be about the same in free ribosomal RNA and in the same acid as a component of the ribosome.

Of prime importance are data on UV hypochromicity of ribosomes or, more exactly, of the RNA contained in the ribosomes. Early experiments (Hall and Doty, 1959) demonstrated that RNA, inside the ribosomes, is hypochromic, i.e., it may contain some helical regions held together by hydrogen bonds. It was further shown that on heating of ribosome solutions such areas "melt," as they do in free RNA. In 1960, a quantitative comparison of hypochromicity in RNA contained in ribosomes and in isolated acid was attempted by several research teams (Zubay and Wilkins; Schlessinger; Bonhoeffer and Schachman). Free acid in solutions of high ionic strength and RNA contained in ribosomes were found to have the same degree of hypochromicity. The experiments also showed about the same number of helical regions and percentage of spiralized nucleotides for free RNA in a coiled state and for bound RNA inside the ribosomes. It may be inferred, by analogy, that the data on the secondary structure of RNA in solution apply equally to the same acid when present in ribosomes. It is further concluded, by extension, that in ribosomes the basic features of the secondary RNA structure, as revealed by the free acid, remain undisturbed and unimpaired by the interaction of the acid with ribosomal protein.

Another group of data were yielded by X-ray investigations of the ribosome structure (Zubay and Wilkins, 1960; Klug et al., 1961). It was shown that the diffraction pattern obtained for the ribosomes was practically identical with the composite pattern produced by superposing an X-ray picture of isolated RNA upon a picture of free ribosomal protein. Analysis of X-ray patterns obtained for the ribosome disclosed the presence of an RNA structure containing helical regions of the same type and conformation as noted for free RNA in solutions. Such areas appeared to be of a double-stranded (double helix) type, with antiparallel chains, and some AU and GC pairs as the predominant type of base pairing in the chain.

Thus, exploring the internal structure of ribosomes by different methods leads to the same conclusion. The secondary RNA structure inside RNP particles (ribosomes) bears considerable resemblance to that found in free high-polymeric RNA in solutions containing salts in moderate concentrations. The above considerations concerning the nature of this structure may apply also in the case of RNA existing in native functioning formations.

2. INTRARIBOSOMAL CHAIN ARRANGEMENT

The ribosomal particles are constituted as highly compact formations whose shape is almost spherical.

Electron microscope observations of Huxley and Zubay (1960) disclosed no preferential location of ribosomal protein or ribosomal RNA either on the periphery or in the center of the ribosomal particle. It would seem, therefore, that both the protein and RNA are uniformly distributed through the entire mass of the ribosome, interpenetrating each other. No protein membrane or layer consisting of pure protein was found along the periphery. (In a virus particle, on the other hand, the RNA is concentrated in the central portion, forming the nuclein nucleus of the particle, while the protein, in the form of a dense membrane, extends along the periphery, enveloping the RNA chain and thus protecting it from contact with the ambient medium.) This suggests that the protein molecules, as a rule, are more or less uniformly distributed through the RNA, so that the coiled RNA chain has some neighboring protein material located along its entire length. It can be assumed that both the secondary and tertiary RNA structure, in ribosomes, are built along the same principles as in the case of RNA in solution. Presumably, they consist basically of consecutively arranged helical regions alternating with randomly structured areas, either "stacked up" or forming a rod (shown in Fig. 15 as structure C). The compact configuration of the ribosome (or its subunits) can then be visualized as a rod-shaped structure enveloped or "impregnated" by protein molecules. The rod, furthermore, is rolled into a compact mass and tightly coiled, forming a nearly spherical particle, identified as the ribosome. This would account for the apparent uniform interpenetration of protein and RNA in the ribosomes.

In line with this assumption, it is of interest that Beer et al. (1960), having achieved a partial destruction of ribosomes by "Versene" treatment, observed under the electron microscope the appearance of some rod-shaped structures ("short fibrils," thickness about 20 Å). These formations seemed to remain attached to the still-intact portion of the ribosome or to be protruding from it. Occasionally such a "fibril" was seen to join two partially destroyed 50S and 30S particles. The over-all impression is that in a partially destroyed ribosome, its RNA or the RNA enveloped by protein will readily assume a rod-shaped configuration.

In experiments carried out by us jointly with N. A. Kiselev, R. S. Shakulov, A. A. Bogdanov and G. G. Gauze, we likewise observed the emergence of similar short strands following treatment of ribosomes, prefixed in formaldehyde, with urea or with sodium dodecyl sulfate in small concentrations. The fact that such strands could be distinguished and compared with the aid of phosphotungstic acid suggests that they contained some protein along with the RNA. These fibrils, in other words, were of a ribonucleoprotein nature.

The principal difficulty in attempting to achieve any controllable structural change in a ribosome in solution involves the following considerations. Any type of action affecting the ribosome and causing an impairment of its native structure will immediately activate the ribonuclease which is a latent component of the ribosome particles. The activation will, in turn, lead invariably to a rapid degradation of ribosomal RNA and of the particle as a whole. Recently, we have been able to overcome this difficulty by removing the latent ribonuclease from the ribosome prior to experimentation. The procedure consisted in washing the ribosomes with an ammonium chloride solution. When such "ribonuclease-free" ribosomes were transferred to solutions of low ionic strength, free of magnesium ions, we were able to observe the unfolding of some formerly compact particles, now stretched into long strands of ribonucleoprotein, 30–40 Å in diameter. No degradation of the nuclein or the protein component was necessary (Spirin et al., 1963). The first sign of such unfolding was a change in the hydrodynamic properties of the ribosomes, indicated by diminished sedimentation coefficients and a simultaneous marked increase in viscosity. Chemical analysis of "unfolded" ribosomes gave 60% RNA and 40% protein, i.e., the same ratio as found in the original, normal ribosomal particles. When isolated from the "unfolded" ribosomes and analyzed in an ultracentrifuge, the RNA was seen to consist of the same two high-molecular components (23S or 17S) which constitute the RNA obtained from native ribosomes. It is evident from these observations that the diminution of sedimentation coefficients noted for "ribonuclease-free" ribosomes, when transferred to water free of magnesium, cannot be attributed to any degradation of these particles into smaller fragments or to any appreciable loss of the structural protein. The decline merely reflects the unfolding process which involves each particle as a whole, but in such a manner that the chain of ribosomal RNA remains continuous and otherwise intact. The unfolding of ribosomal subunits into ribonucleoprotein fibrils, in ribosomes transferred to aqueous magnesium-free solutions, was conclusively demonstrated by electron microscopy. In external appearance, the RNP fibrils bore a close resemblance to the rod-shaped configuration of high-polymeric RNA (see electron microphotographs in Figs. 16-18). In this case, however, as stated above, the fibrils contained 40% protein (found also in normal ribosomes). The unfolding was found to be reversible, inasmuch as the compact ribosomal subunits reappeared on addition of magnesium ions, in sufficient concentrations, to the solution.

Our latest data (Spirin, Kiselev et al., 1963) thus furnish direct evidence that each ribosomal particle (more exactly, each 50S or 30S subunit) is constituted as a ribonucleoprotein fibril coiled in a specific way. The principal portion of the fibril can be visualized as a single molecule of ribosomal RNA, having a rod-shaped configuration, with some helical regions oriented, most likely, at right angles to the direction of the fibril. It is possible that the molecules of ribosomal protein are linked to the RNA molecules in such a way that they do not cause any serious disturbance of the RNA conformation, which results from intramolecular interaction within the acid itself. The protein may penetrate the grooves of the helices, or it may be packed in the space between the helical regions, with the resulting "impregnation" of the RNA rod (strand) by protein. The uniform distribution of protein along the entire length of the rod leads to the formation of a ribonucleoprotein fibril. The latter is folded in a specifically ordered manner, thus forming a compact structure—a ribosomal subunit, either 50S or 30S, depending on the length of the fibril. A model demonstrating a possible arrangement of an RNP fibril in the ribosomal particle was proposed (Spirin, Kiselev et al., 1963).

Chapter V

CONCLUSIONS

In summing up, it should be emphasized that the author does not wish to suggest in any way that the problems concerning the macromolecular structure of RNA have largely been solved. It must be kept in mind that the data and considerations presented in this volume are essentially of a qualitative and descriptive nature. Moreover, even these qualitative interpretations and propositions cannot be regarded as definitive, hence many of the questions posed are still open for discussion. The issues awaiting a final solution need not be listed, but some of them perhaps merit special attention.

The central problem involves the biological significance of the macromolecular RNA structure. The relationship between the macrostructure and the biological functions remains an obscure matter, even though its implications are of paramount importance for molecular biology. Equally unclear is the significance of the specific consecutive arrangement of nucleotides in this macromolecular structure. The same can be said of the basic features common to all conformations of RNA chains which are being studied by physicochemical methods. The degree of spiralization, the length of the helical regions, the specific and nonspecific pairing of bases, the degree of perfection attained by the helices in native RNA, as well as other questions involving the secondary structure, remain a matter of conflicting opinion or considerations based on conjecture. As to the tertiary structure, such information as is available is clearly of a rudimentary nature, so that in the present volume the author was compelled to depend almost exclusively on his own experimental findings. Further extensive research is needed, which will confirm or refute some of the early assumptions. Only then will it be possible to reach a few definitive and more justifiable conclusions with regard to a number of points which have never been properly clarified. The author can only hope that this volume will stimulate an interest in further experimentation and discussion, which might prove useful in developing more clearly defined and quantitatively more precise concepts.

REFERENCES

Allen, E. H., E. Glassman, E. Cordes and R. S. Schweet. 1960. J. Biol. Chem., 235, 1068.

Aronson, A. I. and B. J. McCarthy. 1961. Biophys. J., 1, 215.

Beaven, G. H., E. R. Holiday and E. A. Johnson. 1955. In "The Nucleic Acids," E. Chargaff, J. N. Davidson, eds., v. 1, N. Y., Acad. Press, p. 493.

Beer, M., P. J. Highton and B. J. McCarthy. 1960. J. Mol. Biol., 2, 447.

Belozerskiy, A. N. and A. S. Spirin. 1960. "The Nucleic Acids" (E. Chargaff and J. N. Davidson, eds.). Vol. 3, pp. 147-185. Academic Press, N. Y. In the book: "The Nucleic Acids" IL(Foreign Literature Press). 1962. pp. 123-155.

Bock, R. and W. Stanley, Jr. 1962. Personal Communication.

Boedtker, H. 1959. Biochim. et biophys. acta, 32, 519.

Boedtker, H. 1960. J. Mol. Biol., 2, 171.

Boedtker, H., W. Möller and P. Doty. 1961. Textes condensés des rapports de Colloque internat. sur les acides ribonucléiques et les polyphosphates. Strasbourg, 6-12 juillet 1961.

Boedtker, H., W. Möller and E. Klemperer. 1962. Nature, 194, 444.

Bogdanova, Ye. S., L. P. Gavrilova, G. A. Dvorkin, N. A. Kiselev and A. S. Spirin. 1962. Biokhimiya, 27, 387.

Bonhoeffer, F. and H. K. Schachman. 1960. Biochem. and Biophys. Res., Commun. 2, 366.

Brown, G. L. and G. Zubay. 1960. J. Mol. Biol., 2, 287.

Brown, R. A., K. A. O. Ellem and J. S. Colter. 1960. Nature, 187, 509.

Cheng, P.-Y. 1957. Nature, 179, 426.

Cheng, P.-Y. 1959a. Nature, 184, 190.

Cheng, P.-Y. 1959b. Proc. Nat. Acad. Sci. U. S. A., 45, 1557.
Cheng, P.-Y. 1960. Biochim. et biophys. acta, 37, 238.
Cheo, P. C., B. S. Friesen and R. L. Sinsheimer. 1959. Proc. Nat. Acad. Sci. U. S. A., 45, 305.
Cohen, S. S. and W. M. Stanley. 1942. J. Biol. Chem., 144, 589.
Cox, R. A., A. S. Jones, G. E. Marsh and A. R. Peacocke. 1956. Biochim. et biophys. acta, 21, 576.
Cox, R. A. and U. Z. Littauer. 1959. Nature, 184, 818.
Cox, R. A. and U. Z. Littauer. 1960. J. Mol. Biol., 2, 166.
Danon, D., Y. Marikovsky and U. Z. Littauer. 1961. J. Biophys. and Biochem. Cytol., 9, 253.
Doty, P. 1959a. Proc. IV Internat. Congr. Biochem. Vienna, 1958, v. 8. London, Pergamon Press, p. 8.
Doty, P. 1959b. Rev. Mod. Phys., 31, 107; "Current Problems in Biophysics," Vol. 1, IL (Foreign Literature Press), 1961, pp. 138-151.
Doty, P. Report on the V Intern. Biochem. Congr. Moscow, 10-16 August, 1961. Symposium 1.
Doty, P., H. Boedtker, J. R. Fresco, R. Haselkorn and M. Litt. 1959a. Proc. Nat. Acad. Sci. U. S. A., 45, 482.
Doty, P., H. Boedtker, J. R. Fresco, B. D. Hall and R. Haselkorn. 1959b. Ann. N. Y. Acad. Sci., 81, 693.
Doty, P., A. M. Holtzer, J. H. Bradbury and E. R. Blout. 1954. J. Amer. Chem. Soc., 76, 4493.
Doty, P. and R. D. Lundberg. 1957. Proc. Nat. Acad. Sci. U. S. A., 43, 213.
Duggan, E. L., V. L. Stevens and B. W. Grunbaum. 1957. J. Amer. Chem. Soc., 79, 4859.
Dunn, D. B. 1959. Biochim. et biophys. acta, 34, 286.
Dunn, D. B., J. D. Smith and P. F. Spahr. 1960. J. Mol. Biol., 2, 113.
Dvorkin, G. A. 1960. Dokl. Akad. Nauk SSSR, 135, 739.
Dvorkin, G. A. 1961. Biofizika, 6, 403.
Dvorkin, G. A. and V. I. Krinskiy. 1961. Dokl. Akad. Nauk SSSR, 140, 942.
Dvorkin, G. A. and A. S. Spirin. 1960. Dokl. Akad. Nauk SSSR, 135, 987.
Eisenberg, H. and U. Z. Littauer. 1958. Bull. Res. Council Israel, 7A, 115.
Elson, D. and E. Chargaff. 1955. Biochim. et biophys. acta, 17, 367.
Felsenfeld, G. 1958. Biochim. et biophys. acta, 29, 133.
Felsenfeld, G. and A. Rich. 1957. Biochim. et biophys. acta, 26, 457.

Fraenkel-Conrat, H. 1959. Trans. Faraday Soc., 55, 494.
Fraenkel-Conrat, H. and B. Singer. 1959a. Proc. IV Internat. Congr. Biochem., Vienna, 1958, v. 7. London, Pergamon Press, p. 9.
Fraenkel-Conrat, H. and B. Singer. 1959b. Biochim. et biophys. acta, 33, 359.
Fraenkel-Conrat, H., B. Singer and T. Sugiyama. 1962. Colloque internat. sur les acides ribonicléiques et les polyphosphates. Strasbourg, 6-12 juillet 1961. Paris, C. N. R. S., p. 241.
Fraenkel-Conrat, H., B. Singer and R. C. Williams. 1957. Biochim. et biophys. acta, 25, 87.
Fresco, J. R. and B. M. Alberts. 1960. Proc. Nat. Acad. Sci. U. S. A., 46, 311.
Fresco, J. R., B. M. Alberts and P. Doty. 1960. Nature, 188, 98.
Fresco, J. R. and P. Doty. 1957. J. Amer. Chem. Soc., 79, 3928.
Fresco, J. R., A. M. Lesk, R. Gorn and P. Doty. 1961. J. Amer. Chem. Soc., 83, 3155.
Friesen, B. S. and R. L. Sinsheimer. 1959. J. Mol. Biol., 1, 321.
Frisch-Niggemeyer, W. 1956. Nature, 178, 307.
Frisman, E., V. I. Vorob'yev, N. K. Yanovskaya and L. V. Shchagina. 1963. Biokhimiya, 28, 137.
Fuwa, K., W. E. C. Wacker, R. Druyan, A. F. Bartholomay and B. L. Valee. 1960. Proc. Nat. Acad. Sci. U. S. A., 46, 1298.
Gavrilova, L. P. and A. S. Spirin. 1959. Biokhimiya, 24, 503.
Gavrilova, L. P., A. S. Spirin and A. N. Belozerskiy. 1959. Dokl. Akad. Nauk USSR, 126, 1121.
Gierer, A. 1957. Nature, 179, 1297.
Gierer, A. 1958a. Z. Naturforsch., 13b, 477.
Gierer, A. 1958b. Z. Naturforsch., 13b, 485.
Gierer, A. 1958c. Z. Naturforsch., 13b, 788.
Gierer, A. and G. Schramm. 1956a. Nature, 177, 702.
Gierer, A. and G. Schramm. 1956b. Z. Naturforsch., 11b, 138.
Ginoza, W. 1958. Nature, 181, 958.
Ginoza, W. 1959. Trans. Faraday Soc., 55, 493.
Ginoza, W. and A. Norman. 1957. Nature, 179, 520.
Green, M. and B. Hall. 1961. Biophys. J., 1, 517.
Grinnan, E. L. and W. A. Mosher. 1951. J. Biol. Chem., 191, 719.
Gros, F., W. Gilbert, H. H. Hiatt, G. Attardi, P. F. Spahr and J. D. Watson. 1961. Cold Spring Harbor Sympos. on Quant. Biol., 26, 111.
Gros, F., H. H. Hiatt, W. Gilbert, C. G. Kurland, R. W. Risebrough and J. D. Watson. 1961. Nature, 190, 581.
Habermann, V. 1960. Biochim. et biophys. acta, 41, 521.

Hall, B. D. and P. Doty. 1958. In: "Microsomal particles and protein synthesis," R. B. Roberts, ed., London—N. Y.—Paris —Los Angeles, Pergamon Press, p. 27.
Hall, B. D. and P. Doty. 1959. J. Mol. Biol., 1, 111.
Hall, C. E. 1959. Proc. 4th Internat. Congr. Biochem., Vienna, 1958, v. 9. London, Pergamon Press, p. 20.
Hart, R. G. 1955. Proc. Nat. Acad. Sci. U. S. A., 41, 261.
Hart, R. G. 1958. Biochim. et biophys. acta, 28, 457.
Haschemeyer, R., B. Singer and H. Fraenkel-Conrat. 1959. Proc. Nat. Acad. Sci. U. S. A., 45, 313.
Haselkorn, R. 1962. J. Mol. Biol., 4, 357.
Hecht, L. I., P. C. Zamecnik, M. L. Stephenson and J. F. Scott. 1958. J. Biol. Chem., 233, 954.
Helmkamp, G. K. and P. O. P. Ts'o. 1961. J. Amer. Chem. Soc., 83, 138.
Herbert, E. and E. S. Canellakis. 1960. Biochim. et biophys. acta, 42, 363.
Hiatt, H. H. 1962. J. Mol. Biol., 5, 217.
Hoagland, M. B. 1960. "The Nucleic Acids." E. Chargaff and J. N. Davidson, eds. Vol. 3, N. Y. Acad. Press, p. 349; In the book: "The Nucleic Acids." IL(Foreign Literature Press), 1962, pp. 219-337.
Hopkins, G. R. and R. L. Sinsheimer. 1955. Biochim. et biophys. acta, 17, 476.
Huxley, H. E. and G. Zubay. 1960. J. Mol. Biol., 2, 10.
Ishihama, A., N. Mizuno, M. Takai, E. Otaka and S. Osawa. 1962. J. Mol. Biol., 5, 251.
Kay, E. R. M. and A. L. Dounce. 1953. J. Amer. Chem. Soc., 75, 4041.
Kirby, K. S. 1956. Biochem. J., 64, 405.
Kiselev, L. L., Ye. P. Rebinder and L. Yu. Frolova. 1962a. High Molecular Compounds (Vysokomolekulyarnyye soyedineniya), 4, 755.
Kiselev, L. L., L. Yu. Frolova and Ye. P. Rebinder. 1962b. High Molecular Compounds (Vysokomolekulyarnyye soyedineniya), 4, 749.
Kiselev, N. A., L. P. Gavrilova and A. S. Spirin. 1961a. Dokl. Akad. Nauk USSR, 138, 692.
Kiselev, N. A., L. P. Gavrilova and A. S. Spirin. 1961b. J. Mol. Biol., 3, 778.
Kiselev, N. A. and L. L. Kiselev. 1961. Dokl. Akad. Nauk SSSR, 141, 980.
Klug, A., K. C. Holmes and J. T. Finch. 1961. J. Mol. Biol., 3, 87.

Kronman, M. J., S. N. Timashev, J. S. Colter and R. A. Brown. 1960. Biochim. et biophys. acta, 40, 410.
Kurland, C. G. 1960. J. Mol. Biol., 2, 83.
Laland, S. C., W. A. Lee, W. G. Overend and A. B. Peacocke. 1954. Biochim. et biophys. acta, 14, 356.
Laskov, R., E. Margoliash, U. Z. Littauer and H. Fisenberg. 1959. Biochim. et biophys. acta, 33, 247.
Littauer, U. Z. 1961. In "Protein biosynthesis," Proc. UNESCO Sympos. Wassenaar. Netherlands, 1960. R. J. C. Harris, ed. N. Y., Acad. Press, p. 143.
Littauer, U. Z., D. Danon and Y. Marikovsky. 1960. Biochim. et biophys. acta, 42, 435.
Littauer, U. Z. and H. Eisenberg. 1958. Bull. Res. Council Israel, 7A, 114.
Littauer, U. Z. and H. Eisenberg. 1959. Biochim. et biophys. acta, 32, 320.
Loring, H. S., S. Al-Rawi and Y. Fujimoto. 1958. J. Biol. Chem., 233, 1415.
Loring, H. S. and R. S. Waritz. 1957. Science, 125, 64b.
Magasanik, B. 1955. In "The Nucleic Acids," E. Chargaff, J. N. Davidson, eds. v. 1. N. Y., Acad. Press, p. 373.
Möller, W. and H. Boedtker. 1961. Federat. Proc., 20, 357.
Möller, W. and H. Boedtker. 1962. Colloque internat. sur les acides ribonucléiques et polyphosphates. Strasbourg, 6-12 juillet 1961. Paris, C. N. R. S., p. 99.
Monier, R., S. Naono, D. Hayes, F. Hayes and F. Gros. 1962. J. Mol. Biol., 5, 311.
Nomura, M., B. D. Hall and S. Spiegelman. 1960. J. Mol. Biol., 2, 306.
Northrop, T. G. and R. L. Sinsheimer. 1954. J. Chem. Phys., 22, 703.
O'Konski, C. T. and A. J. Haltner. 1957. J. Amer. Chem. Soc., 79, 5634.
Osawa, S. 1960. Biochim. et biophys. acta, 43, 110.
Preiss, J., P. Berg, E. J. Ofengand, F. H. Bergmann and J. Diekmann. 1959. Proc. Nat. Acad. Sci. U. S. A., 45, 319.
Reddi, K. K. 1958. Biochim. et biophys. acta, 27, 1.
Rice, R. V. 1961. Biochim. et biophys. acta, 53, 29.
Rich, A. and D. R. Davies. 1956. J. Amer. Chem. Soc., 78, 3548.
Rich, A. and J. D. Watson. 1954a. Nature, 173, 995.
Rich, A. and J. D. Watson. 1954b. Proc. Nat. Acad. Sci. U. S. A., 40, 759.
Scherrer, K. and J. E. Darnell. 1962. Biochem. and Biophys. Res. Commun., 7, 486.

Schlessinger, D. 1960. J. Mol. Biol., 2, 92.
Schuster, H. 1960. In: "The Nucleic Acids," E. Chargaff, J. N. Davidson, eds., Vol. 3. N. Y. Acad. Press, p. 245; In the book: "The Nucleic Acids," IL(Foreign Literature Press), 1962, pp. 205-253.
Seeds, W. 1953. Progr. Biophys. and Biophys. Chem., 3, 27.
Shakulov, R. S., M. A. Aytkhozhin and A. S. Spirin. 1962. Biokhimiya, 27, 744.
Singer, M. F. and G. L. Cantoni. 1960. Biochim. et biophys. acta, 39, 182.
Spencer, M., W. Fuller, M. H. F. Wilkins and G. L. Brown. 1962. Nature, 194, 1014.
Spiegelman, S. 1961. Cold Spring Harbor Sympos. Quant. Biol., 26, 75.
Spirin, A. S. 1960. J. Mol. Biol., 2, 436.
Spirin, A. S. 1961a. Biokhimiya, 26, 511.
Spirin, A. S. 1961b. Textes condensés des rapports de Colloque Intern. sur les acides ribonucléiques et les polyphosphates. Strasbourg, 6-12 juillet 1961.
Spirin, A. S. 1962a. Colloque Intern. sur les acides ribonucléiques et les polyphosphates. Strasbourg, 6-12 juillet 1961, p. 73, CNRS Paris.
Spirin, A. S. 1962b. Proc. V Intern. Biochem. Congress Moscow, 10-16 August 1961. Symposium 1, p. 99. Moscow, Izd-vo Akad. Nauk USSR.
Spirin, A. S. and L. P. Gavrilova. 1958. Abstracts of Reports of the X All-Union Conference on High Molecular Compounds. Izd-vo Akad. Nauk USSR, 1958, p. 25.
Spirin, A. S. and L. P. Gavrilova. 1961. Izv. Akad. Nauk SSSR, seriya biol., No. 4, 504.
Spirin, A. S., L. P. Gavrilova and A. N. Belozerskiy. 1959. Dokl. Akad. Nauk USSR, 125, 658.
Spirin, A. S., L. P. Gavrilova, S. Ye. Bresler and M. I. Mosevitskiy. 1959. Biokhimiya, 24, 938.
Spirin, A. S., N. A. Kiselev, R. S. Shakulov and A. A. Bogdanov. 1963. Biokhimiya, 28, 920.
Spirin, A. S. and L. S. Mil'man. 1960. Dokl. Akad. Nauk SSSR, 134, 717.
Strohmaier, K. and M. Mussgay. 1959. Z. Naturforsch., 14b, 171.
Takai, M., H. Kondo and S. Osawa. 1962. Biochim. et biophys. acta, 55, 416.
Takanami, M. 1960. Biochim. et biophys. acta, 39, 152.
Tashiro, Y., H. Shimidzu, A. Inouye and K. Kakiuchi. 1960. Biochim. et biophys. acta, 43, 544.

Thomas, R. 1954. Biochim. et biophys. acta, 14, 231.
Thorell, B. and F. Ruch. 1951. Nature, 167, 815.
Timashev, S. N., R. A. Brown, J. S. Colter and M. Davies. 1958. Biochim. et biophys. acta, 27, 662.
Timashev, S. N., J. Witz and V. Luzzati. 1961. Biophys. J., 1, 525.
Tissieres, A. 1959. J. Mol. Biol., 1, 365.
Tissieres, A. and J. D. Watson. 1958. Nature, 182, 778.
Tissieres, A., J. D. Watson, D. A. Schlessinger and B. R. Hollingworth. 1959. J. Mol. Biol., 1, 221.
Ts'o, P. O. P. 1958. In "Microsomal particles and protein synthesis," R. B. Roberts, ed. London—N. Y.—Paris—Los Angeles, Pergamon Press, p. 156.
Ts'o, P. O. P. and G. Helmkamp. 1961. Tetrahedron, 13, 198.
Ts'o, P. O. P. and R. Squires. 1959. Federat. Proc., 18, 341.
Ts'o, P. O. P., F. W. Studier, I. Melvin, G. K. Helmkamp and C. Sander. 1960. A report for the year 1959-1960 on the research of the Division of Biology at the California Institute of Technology.
Volkin, E. and C. E. Carter. 1951. J. Amer. Chem. Soc., 73, 1516.
Wacker, W. E. C. and B. L. Vallee. 1959. J. Biol. Chem., 234, 3257.
Wallace, J. M. and P. O. P. Ts'o. 1961. Biochem. and Biophys. Res. Commun., 5, 125.
Warner, R. C. 1957. J. Biol. Chem., 229, 711.
Wecker, E. 1959. Z. Naturforsch., 14b, 370.
Zillig, W., D. Schachtschabel and W. Krone. 1960. Z. physiol. Chem., 318, 100.
Zubay, G. and M. H. F. Wilkins. 1960. J. Mol. Biol., 2, 105.

Part II

MACROMOLECULAR STRUCTURE OF RIBONUCLEIC ACIDS AND BIOLOGICAL FUNCTION

Chapter I

THE NUCLEOTIDE COMPOSITION AND FUNCTIONS OF THE RIBONUCLEIC ACIDS

In 1958, A. N. Belozersky [1] reported some data concerning the nucleotide composition of the RNA's found in microorganisms, as compared with the DNA composition. In the same study some important points were elucidated regarding the RNA functions. In the past six years it has been possible to evaluate these findings even more closely, in the light of the most recent advances in the study of the nucleic acids. The principal results of the abovementioned research will be summarized briefly.

Recent years, beginning with the early 50's, mark the development of new microanalytical methods in biochemistry and the use of new preparative techniques, as well as a number of unexpected discoveries. The identification of DNA as a factor in bacterial transformations is a case in point. All of this has contributed materially to further advances in determining the structure and biological functions of the nucleic acids. The specificity of these acids was, for the first time, made a point of discussion in the early investigations of that period. Successful studies of protein biosynthesis, on the one hand, and broad research in genetics, on the other, have helped in the shaping of some clearly defined concepts with regard to the template role of nucleic acids in protein synthesis. In these concepts the specificity of the nucleic acid molecules is seen as a decisive factor that determines the specificity of proteins synthesized in the cell. The nucleic acid chain here provides a template on which the polypeptide chain of the protein is built, so that a definite amino acid, in the chain of a newly formed protein, corresponds to each specific combination of nucleotides in the template. The nature of cell proteins is thus determined by the specific structure of nucleic acids normally present in the cell, which is to say that the metabolism and biological properties of the cell are determined by the specific structure of nucleic acids peculiar to a given cell. This emphasized the importance of nucleic acids as a genetic factor, for which some corroborating evidence had been obtained in unrelated experiments as well. Most significantly, so far as the understanding of nucleic acid functions is concerned, it has been shown that of the two types of nucleic acids, RNA and DNA, it is the DNA that is a decisive primary factor in determining the specificity of synthesized proteins and in transmitting such specificity from one generation to the next. Conversely, in all investigations of the direct biochemical mechanisms involved in protein synthesis, direct participation of RNA in the protein molecule formation has been immediately apparent. An outgrowth of such accumulated evidence was a widely acknowledged and fruitful hypothesis in which RNA was seen as the direct template in protein synthesis, with a template for RNA synthesis provided in turn by DNA. In other words, the latter acid was assumed to control the specificity of protein synthesis indirectly, through the specific RNA's synthesized on DNA, as the actual direct participants in the synthesis of proteins.

The specificity of nucleic acids has been rather prominently involved in the experimental elaboration of these concepts. The basic technique employed consisted of determining the quantitative ratios of nucleotides to nucleic acids, i.e., defining the base composition of these acids. The base composition of DNA's found in the organisms of different species was studied for the first time in the USA. The experiments, conducted in the laboratory of E. Chargaff [37], demonstrated a species-determined specificity of DNA composition. The DNA's obtained from different species were shown to differ in the weight ratios of their four nitrogenous bases. Similar studies were carried out by us in the laboratory of A. N. Belozersky, where a distinct specificity of base composition was demonstrated for DNA's obtained from various species of bacteria [19]. Differences in the DNA composition between one species and another could be very pronounced, but they diminished progressively for species close to each other biologically and in their systemic position. Some correlation thus seemed to exist between DNA composition and the inherited biological properties of a given species [19, 3, 4]. These findings were consistent with the emergent concept of DNA as a genetic factor and a determinant of protein specificity. This was important evidence in confirming the validity of propositions discussed above.

By that time enough facts had been gathered to indicate that DNA functioned indirectly through RNA, rather than directly through proteins. It seemed perfectly reasonable, in those relatively recent years, to assume that the nucleotide composition of RNA in any given species must reflect more or less closely the nucleotide composition of DNA or, at any rate, display the same degree of species-determined specificity. The validity of this rather obvious assumption was never questioned—so much so that specificity studies of nucleic acids dating back to this period were centered largely on DNA, while RNA was practically "ignored." In our own work, however, parallel experiments on RNA composition were run, as a sort of extracurricular research venture, simultaneously with DNA composition studies on bacteria [18, 19, 21].

Our earliest important observation was that RNA composition in the various bacterial species did not in any way reflect the broad variations of DNA composition from one species to another; i.e., it seemed independent of DNA specificity. RNA composition, unlike that of DNA, was shown to be remarkably similar in different species. This observation has influenced significantly the subsequent shaping of concepts defining the biological functions of nucleic acids. To begin with, it invalidated the neat hypothesis wherein cell RNA was treated as a mere reflection or replica patterned after DNA, whose chief function was to transmit information from DNA to proteins synthesized on RNA as a template. In this connection, F. Crick wrote in 1959:* "The coding problem has so far passed through three phases. In the first, the vague phase, various suggestions were made, but none was sufficiently precise to admit disproof. The second phase, the optimistic phase, was initiated by Gamow in 1954, who was rash enough to suggest a fairly precise code. This stimulated a number of workers to show that his suggestions must be incorrect and, in doing so, increased somewhat the precision of thinking in this field. The third phase, the confused phase, was initiated by the paper of Belozersky and Spirin in 1958, although the experimental data had actually been

*The quoted passage is not a translation. It was copied verbatim from Crick's original report (in English).—Tr.

published earlier, both by them and by Lee, Wahl and Barbu. The evidence presented there showed that our ideas were in some important respects too simple" [38].

Besides this negative aspect of the above data on RNA composition, the same research work brought to light *another important fact*, which, however, remained practically unnoticed at the time. While no significant variations of RNA composition, and no direct correlation with DNA, could be demonstrated, comparison of data obtained for different species revealed a distinct tendency toward a change in the same direction as noted for DNA composition [19, 2]. A marked difference in DNA composition between different species, say, an increased ratio "(guanine + cytosine) : (adenine + thymine)," was associated with a simultaneous, statistically reliable, if very slight, shift in RNA composition toward an increased ratio "(guanine + cytosine) : (adenine + uracil)." A positive correlation between RNA and DNA composition was thus shown to exist, though the magnitude of RNA regression (shift) proved very slight when compared with that of DNA. The author concluded, as did A. N. Belozersky, that the total RNA of a bacterial cell was not functionally homogeneous. In addition to the bulk of RNA relatively nonspecific with respect to different species, it was thought expedient to include a small RNA fraction whose nucleotide composition was homologous with that of cellular DNA [19, 2]. The conclusion suggested for the first time the existence of a specific, DNA-like fraction of RNA contained in small quantities by a normal cell. In 1958, it was stated explicitly that "the RNA fraction correlating with DNA may conceivably function as a connecting link, in the sense that it transmits inherited information from DNA to some other substrates of the cell, possibly proteins" [1].

Today we know this to be true. In the past six years it has been demonstrated in laboratories of every description the world over that cellular RNA is subdivided into a number of functionally distinct RNA types, i.e., functionally different fractions. The fraction dominant by weight is high-polymeric ribosomal RNA, which is a structural component of ribosomes or ribonucleoprotein particles (RNP-particles) [52]. According to present-day views, the ribosomes are the intracellular centers of protein synthesis. They constitute the basic protein-synthesizing system within which the specific polypeptide chain is formed from activated amino acids. The entire spectrum of processes culminating in this formation develops in the same system. Since the bulk of total RNA in the cell (about 80%) consists of ribosomal RNA, data on regularities governing the composition of this acid were inevitably the first ones obtained in our composition studies of total cell RNA. Some conclusions could therefore be drawn relating specifically to this acid. Unlike DNA, ribosomal RNA exhibited no marked, species-determined changes and no general conformity with DNA in composition. In the light of this observation it seemed rather unlikely that ribosomal RNA alone could provide a specific structural template for protein synthesis in the ribosomes. Nothing definite is known, in fact, concerning the biological role of ribosomal RNA. One thing is clear, however. Together with structural ribosomal proteins, it participates in the shaping of ribosomal particles, hence it must be intact if the ribosomes are to function as a system in which protein synthesis takes place.

Recent direct experiments have shown that a template for protein synthesis in ribosomes is provided, in effect, by the relatively small RNA fraction whose nucleotide composition conforms to that of cellular DNA. In experiments on bacteria, this RNA was directly identified as a separate fraction, isolated, analyzed and studied with respect to its ability to ensure specificity of protein synthesis in the ribosome [32, 48, 67]. This RNA fraction proved the actual "intermediary" between cellular DNA and the protein-synthesizing mechanism of the cell; hence, it was named "messenger" (information) RNA. It is synthesized on a DNA template, consequently, its polynucleotide chain must reproduce a portion of one of the chains in the DNA molecule. In order to participate in protein synthesis, the molecule of messenger RNA, synthesized on a DNA molecule, must become attached to the ribosome. Only in this state, being linked to the ribosome, will it be able to function as a specific template needed for the formation of a polypeptide chain. Nor will the ribosome become active, unless a molecule of messenger RNA has been linked to it. The specificity of synthesized proteins is determined by the type of messenger RNA that has formed a link with the ribosome. It is thus the messenger RNA that is responsible for the specific "programming" of the ribosome.

Ribosomal RNA, according to further evidence, cannot function as a polynucleotide template unless a third type of cellular RNA, the so-called soluble RNA, is present in the ribosome [52]. This acid accounts for about 10-20% of total RNA in the cell. The point is that the amino acids as such display no steric conformity to the nucleotides, or their combinations, in the template and are therefore unable to "decode" the ordered sequence of nucleotides in template RNA. It has been found that the strictly predetermined, specific pattern of their orientation in a polypeptide chain being synthesized in the ribosome is attained through polyribonucleotides of a special type and relatively low molecular weight, rather than by way of direct arrangement of amino acids on a template polynucleotide (of messenger RNA). These unique polyribonucleotides, which are molecules of the "soluble" RNA, act as adaptors facilitating the correct placement of each amino acid in its proper position on the template. The "soluble" RNA molecule is able, with the aid of special enzyme systems, to attach preactivated amino acids to either end of its polynucleotide chain. Only when this happens will these amino acids become capable of participating in protein synthesis taking place in the ribosome. To each type of amino acid corresponds a specific "soluble" RNA molecule. In accordance with the number of native amino acids, there are not less than 20 different kinds of "soluble" RNA in the cell. The binding of amino acids by "soluble" RNA molecules takes place in the cell juice, outside the ribosome. Immediately thereafter the compound "soluble RNA-amino acid" is admitted to the ribosome. In each molecule of the "soluble" RNA, the polynucleotide chain contains a particular small section which sterically conforms (is complementary) to some specific combination of the nucleotides in the polynucleotide chain of the template (messenger RNA). In consequence, a strictly specified type of amino acid corresponds to any given combination of nucleotides on the template. The soluble RNA thus acts as interpreter, translating from the coded language of the nucleotide sequence in nucleic acids into the language of the amino acid sequence in proteins. This is the chief function of "soluble" RNA.

The ribosome is thus seen to consitute a center where information recorded on template RNA is processed (recoded) and a polypeptide chain is built. The material—compounds of amino acids with adaptor ("soluble") RNA—flows from the cell juice into the ribosomes. The information is transmitted from the nucleus to the ribosomes as a continuous stream of molecules of messenger

RNA synthesized on individual sections of DNA. The messenger RNA present in the ribosome provides a specific template that determines the sequential order in which the "soluble" RNA molecules alternate with the amino acids linked to them. This, in turn, determines the sequence of amino acids in the polypeptide chain of the protein in the process of formation.

Chapter II

THE MACROMOLECULAR STRUCTURE OF RIBONUCLEIC ACIDS

It would hardly be an exaggeration to say that we are now a bit dazzled by the enormous advances in understanding the functions of biological macromolecules, nucleic acids in particular. No less overwhelming is the vast scope of pioneering research currently carried on in this field. Yet, we should not lose sight of the fact that, despite the sweeping strides, the present state of our knowledge and the nature of our inquiry are still rudimentary, reflecting, by and large, the first groping attempts to develop this "molecular-biological" trend of research into a full-fledged science. At its present level, it is confined largely, and unavoidably, to mere fact-recording or descriptive probing into the biological functions of the macromolecules. However, having established what specific functions are performed by this or that molecule, we still do not know *how* it does its work. The question concerns the molecular *mechanism* involved in the functioning of the macromolecule of a biopolymer. With respect to either proteins or nucleic acids, the matter has thus far remained practically unexplored.

Evidently, the inherent capacity of certain macromolecules for performing specific functions is based on their essential structure, as governed by certain regularities. Clearly, therefore, the structure of a biological macromolecule must be determined before the mechanism of its functioning (its behavior) can be properly understood. Structural studies are both the necessary premise and a straight road leading in this direction. Our ultimate task is to establish which basic structural features, in any type of biopolymer, determine its specific function. In the ideal case, the knowledge and correct interpretation of molecular structure should tell us what the function of the particular molecule will be under any given set of actual conditions.

A striking example, in this connection, is found in structural studies of DNA. In 1953, J. D. Watson and F. Crick proposed their famous model of a double-stranded macromolecular structure for DNA [17]. One of the major structural features of DNA—*the principle of complementarity* of the nitrogenous bases in the two polynucleotide chains—has for the first time been formulated in this report. The discovery offered an adequate explanation of the ability of DNA to reproduce precisely its specific structure. It could then be understood, in other words, how the exact transmission of specificity from one generation to another, i.e., the DNA function in the cell, was possible at the molecular level [72]. Such was the nature of the structural principle established in this instance that the inherent potential capacity for performing a specific function could be identified directly with the characteristic structure of the macromolecule.

The principle of complementarity discovered by Watson and Crick ensures that interaction of the two polynucleotide chains will be strictly specific. It is also responsible for the specificity of synthesis of the one chain or the other being rigidly predetermined. This principle has been, and still is, most helpful in attempting to understand or explain the various aspects of biological processes which involve participation by nucleic acids. Among these are the synthesis of messenger RNA on DNA; the interaction of adaptor RNA with template RNA (also, other types of interaction between the various RNA's in the ribosome); the formation of secondary structure in RNA; etc.

Unfortunately, not much more is known at this time about the structural basis of the biological functions peculiar to the macromolecules. The above facts are all, or nearly all, we know concerning the exact relationship between structure and function on the molecular level. To begin with, we are still unable to single out those structural principles, in the organization of a protein molecule, which determine a major protein function, the enzymic function. In the case of the DNA's, not to mention the RNA's, there are many aspects of their functioning in the cell, or in the model systems, that cannot possibly be explained on the basis of the complementarity principle alone. With respect to the great variety of RNA's, which appear to be polyfunctional, pinpointing the structural principles that could determine their widely diversified useful functions in the cell is a particularly important task.

Our ultimate research aim is to establish a link between structure and function. Little has been done in this direction, and even the purely descriptive structural studies of the RNA macromolecules have for many years been lagging behind protein and DNA research. One reason for this may be sought in considerable difficulties involved in isolating RNA in a nondegraded state. Another reason is the lack of biological criteria for evaluating nativity. The studies of the macromolecular structure of RNA were, in effect, initiated as late as 1956-1957 by Gierer and Schramm in Germany [46] and by the Fraenkel-Conrat, Singer and Williams research team in the USA [42]. In these experiments high-polymeric RNA was isolated from the tobacco mosaic virus (TMV). It was shown for the first time that the acid itself possesses infectious activity, hence is in a native state from the biological point of view. The possibility of obtaining biologically active, infectious preparations of virus RNA at once attracted the attention of research men. Such RNA could serve as an excellent and, it would seem, relatively simple model for studies of structure in relation to function. Its highly specific, easy-to-test biological activity, furthermore, offered a reliable nativity criterion with respect to virus RNA structure. These considerations prompted the author, in the latter part of 1957, to set up experiments reproducing the previously reported isolation of infectious RNA preparations from TMV. The tests, carried out in collaboration with L. P. Gavrilova, were followed by studies of the macromolecular structure of this isolated, native, virus RNA in solution [7, 8, 12, 20, 22]. Similar studies of the macromolecular structure, conducted on infectious TMV RNA, were undertaken in many laboratories, notably at the laboratory of P. Doty in the United States [29, 30, 40].

The techniques that made possible the isolation of infectious virus RNA in a nondegraded state (above all, the method of phenolic deproteinization) were immediately adopted, and are being used more and more extensively, for obtaining RNA from various cellular organisms—animal, bacterial, and those of higher plants. While continuing our macromolecular studies on virus RNA, we started a series of parallel comparison experiments on isolated high-polymeric RNA. Our experimental material consisted largely of ribosomal RNA from cellular organisms of animal, plant and bacterial origin [24, 13, 5]. The over-all evidence yielded by this research revealed a striking similarity, as well as universality, of the basic principles underlying the structural organization of the macromolecules in widely diversified high-molecular-weight RNA's, examined in an isolated state. In our discussion, therefore, these acids should be treated as a group, without making a distinction between virus and ribosomal RNA's.

In our work we used a combination of physical procedures, as is generally done in studies of the macromolecular structure. The hydrodynamic methods, i.e., sedimentation in the ultracentrifuge combined with viscosity measurements, made it possible to observe the general shape and configuration of RNA particles in solution. Evaluation of the inner structure with respect to regularity was made by measuring the ultraviolet (UV) hypochromic effect and optical activity. A study of UV dichroism exhibited by RNA molecules when oriented in an electric field was carried out jointly with G. A. Dvorkin at the Institute of Biophysics, Academy of Sciences, USSR [9]. As a result, some information was obtained on the preferential arrangement of the chromophore groups (i.e., of the planes coincident with the rings of the nitrogenous bases) relative to the long axis of an RNA particle. Finally, electron microscope studies of RNA macromolecules, conducted in collaboration with N. A. Kisselev at the Institute of Crystallography, Academy of Sciences, USSR [10, 11], made possible the direct observation of the general aspect, shape, size and characteristic configuration of RNA particles.

On the basis of the above experimental findings certain concepts were proposed by us regarding the macromolecular structure of high-polymeric RNA in solution. There would seem to be no point, at this state, in discussing these data at length or comparing them with results obtained in other laboratories. This has already been done, both in relevant reports [12, 20, 16] and, rather more extensively, in a small monograph [17]. The point I should like to stress here is that our aim, from the very outset, was not so much to describe the dimensions, shape and structural organization of RNA macromolecules in a given static state as to achieve structural modification, under certain influencing conditions, and then determine the nature of such changes with the aid of physical methods. In biopolymer studies, this approach could be expected, above all, to help us identify the *essential* structural features, e.g., the features that *determine* the conformation and conformational behavior of the polymer.

1. CONTINUITY OF THE POLYNUCLEOTIDE CHAIN

One of the first important observations yielded by experiments conducted along this line was that RNA macromolecules undergo a structural transition when the solution is heated (the "temperature effect"). The process manifested itself as a stepwise transformation of the compact RNA particle into a straightened or loosely coiled polynucleotide chain [18, 22]. The discovery provided a key to the solution of many related problems involving the macromolecular structure of RNA. One important question that had to be answered, at the time, was whether large RNA macromolecules of the virus or ribosomal type were built as an aggregate of separate, relatively short polynucleotide chains or as a single, continuous polynucleotide chain. In the case of ribosomal RNA's this seemed particularly important. The bulk of the evidence obtained by Doty [49] and other investigators led them to believe that, structurally, the ribosomal RNA's were made up of a variable number of subunits. Our studies of the effect of heating on the state of the macromolecules in ribosomal RNA's demonstrated that this was not so [24, 13, 5]. It was shown that each molecule of a ribosomal RNA whose molecular weight was of the order of 10^6 consisted of a single, *continuous* polynucleotide chain, which under normal conditions was coiled, forming a compact particle. The continuity of the chain was established without much difficulty, thanks to the "temperature effect," i.e., thermal unfolding of the chain. It is obvious that any discontinuity involving a compact "coil" (RNA molecule), in a chain made up of covalent links, will become apparent as the "coil" unfolds into a "strand." In recent years the continuity of polynucleotide chains, in the ribosomal and other high molecular RNA's, has been amply confirmed by other investigators. It can thus be considered proved beyond doubt that the molecules of both ribosomal and virus RNA's are structured of long, continuous polynucleotide chains in which thousands of links (nucleotides) are held together by covalent bonds.

2. SECONDARY STRUCTURE

According to extensive experimental data, the RNA chains in solution are wound into dense, compact particles containing regular helical structures [40, 22, 5, 16]. When the temperature of the solution is raised, these helical structures undergo destruction ("melting" of the secondary structure). The process develops as the solution is being heated, simultaneously with the thermal unfolding of the polynucleotide chain [22, 5]. The "melting" of a helix is reflected in a diminution of optical rotation nearly to zero, as well as in greater UV absorption (decline of hypochromic effect). As seen from all measurement data, RNA's of highly diversified origin, including the virus, ribosomal and "soluble"

RNA's, are fully identical in every basic spiralization feature disclosed by experiments [16].

At the same time, RNA is seen to differ markedly from DNA in some properties of secondary structure. The DNA molecule is a continuous, perfectly shaped double helix, which imparts rigidity to the molecular structure along its entire length. In the case of RNA, on the other hand, the possibility that it may exist in the form of a similarly rigid single helix must be ruled out if we consider the hydrodynamic properties of this acid. The RNA molecule is further shown to consist of a single, continuous polynucleotide chain. What this means is that any secondary structure found in RNA must have formed only as a result of interaction between the links of one chain. (In contrast to this, the DNA molecule is built of two chains, which can be separated by subjecting the acid to denaturation). Consequently, the spiralization of an RNA chain, unlike that of DNA, results from interaction of bases which are confined to one and the same chain. A further point of distinction is the complete and practically instantaneous reversibility of thermal destruction ("melting") of helices in an RNA molecule. The destructive process (denaturation) undergone by DNA is only partially reversible, and then only under special conditions of slow cooling (renaturation). Finally, the most important distinction, observed in all experiments on the "melting" of helical RNA structures, is the absence of sudden transition within a narrow temperature interval, such as will occur characteristically in structural transformations of DNA molecules. An abrupt transition reflects a collective (cooperative) process which involves destruction of a single, uniform (regular) structure. In the case of RNA, transition takes place over a far wider temperature interval than is required for "melting" a single helix of the DNA type, and it indicates rather a successive melting of numerous individual short helices. From these experimental data it is concluded that in RNA molecules spiralization is not complete as in DNA, but partial, and that the secondary structure of RNA in solution is, most likely, an aggregate of relatively short helices which form due to interaction of bases within one and the same chain [40, 22, 44].

Doty et al. [40, 44] showed that in an RNA molecule individual sections of the polynucleotide chain interact with one another in pairs. Such paired interaction is possible because the single-stranded RNA chain is highly flexible, so that various sections of the chain can come in contact with one another. The contacting sections interact because their bases become linked in pairs. Eventually, the interacting sections become wound about each other, and a local double-stranded helical region forms at the site. A very large number of contacts between the different sections of the single-stranded chain is possible in a molecule of high-polymeric RNA. This results in high saturation of RNA molecules with newly formed double-helical regions. There is ample and convincing proof [44, 66] that all, or nearly all, pairing of bases inside an RNA molecule, in solutions kept at room temperature, results from interaction of adenine with uracil (A-U pairs) and guanine with cytosine (G-C pairs). The helical areas, in RNA molecules, form as the chain, or its sections, make a U-turn (fold upon themselves). In each such area, therefore, the strands run in antiparallel directions [40, 44, 66]. Thus, individual helical areas in RNA exhibit some typical DNA-like characteristics, including the A-U and G-C pairs and antiparallel strands.

This description of the secondary RNA structure, based on the literature data as well as our own, fails to emphasize the main distinction which renders RNA one of the most remarkable biological polymers. The secondary RNA structure is not a fixed, predetermined formation possessing some degree of rigidity, such as is generally assumed for protein and DNA molecules. Quite to the contrary, it should be defined as a mobile, flexible, reversibly changeable, balanced structure. Under any given set of actual conditions existing in the solution, the RNA chain acquires *spontaneously* a particular conformation which, under these conditions, corresponds to a state in which the various molecular forces are at equilibrium. This peculiarity was discussed by us in earlier reports [22, 20] for the particular case of TMV RNA. In a TMV particle, high-polymeric RNA exists in the form of a chain supported by the protein component of this virus, which has the shape of a low-pitch (23Å) helix, with an 80Å diameter. The secondary structure of this acid is not fully identical with the one discussed above. Following deproteinization of TMV, the RNA chain is found to be in a free state, and its secondary structure, which emerges spontaneously, is of a nature characteristic for any type of RNA in solution. G. Felsenfeld, working with synthetic polynucleotide models, reported in an earlier communication [41] that complementary pairing of polyribonucleotide chains, or chain sections, involves demonstrably, and specifically, a reversible interaction. This ensures lateral mobility of such chains (sections) relative to each other as they seek the optimal state in terms of energy conservation. J. Fresco and B. Alberts [43], experimenting likewise with polynucleotide models, concluded that in the case of incomplete complementarity, both searching and lateral motion depend essentially on the mutual adjustment of the chains (or their sections). The fitting is achieved by way of loop formation, for which the noncomplementary nucleotides supply the material. It is lateral mobility, in the opinion of Fresco and co-workers [44], that enables an RNA molecule to search out the most stable, i.e., the most advantageous, of the competing conformations. The authors believe this proposition to be basic in considering the secondary structure of RNA in solution. In excellent agreement with these ideas are our own data on the complete and practically instantaneous reversibility of all changes developing in the secondary structure or the general conformation. This refers also to the restoration of all the original characteristics, such as helicity parameters, or the size and shape of the particles, following a complete "melting" of the helices and thermal unfolding of the chain [22, 5]. It might be added that "denaturation," as it is generally understood, is not the proper term to use with respect to RNA in solution, since it has no fixed secondary structure. The latter readily undergoes modification as soon as conditions existing in the solution are altered. It follows that such structural modifications are reversible. A point to be emphasized, however, is that this mobility and reactivity of the conformation, far from doing away with the specificity problem as regards the secondary RNA structure, suggests new possibilities in this direction. The basic operating factor to be considered here is that under any given conditions existing in the solution, each RNA molecule will spontaneously and rapidly assume a secondary structure "pattern" of its own. This pattern will be unique, being rigidly predetermined by the above conditions as well as by the specific nucleotide sequence peculiar to RNA.

3. TERTIARY STRUCTURE

The existence of separate, regular helical structures in macromolecules and the nature of spiralization are matters relating to the secondary structure. In addition to such questions, the study of RNA, as of any other ordered polymer, is concerned also with the possible existence of some regularity pattern governing the mutual orientation and packing of the various parts of the molecule, its helical areas included. The question must be treated with respect to the particle as a whole and is concerned with what has been named, somewhat arbitrarily, the tertiary RNA structure. Some considerations pointing to the absence of a tertiary structure in RNA molecules have been stated in reports published by the laboratory of P. Doty [29, 30, 40]. However, some evidence of positive UV dichroism in the oriented molecules of high-molecular-weight RNA was obtained by Dvorkin and Spirin in 1960 [9]. These data indicated that some degree of order exists in the arrangement of chain links within the RNA molecule, considered as a whole. In addition to establishing the bare fact that the RNA macromolecule, when in solution, possesses to some extent an ordered structure, the same experiments revealed the actual nature of this order. The planes in which the rings of the bases lie were shown to be arranged mostly parallel to the long axis of the molecule. If available information on the secondary RNA structure, with the characteristic double-stranded helical areas, is taken as a basis, an arrangement of such regions at right angles to the long axis of the particle can easily be visualized. In this case the arrangement of the planes coincident with the nitrogenous bases will indeed be parallel with respect to the axis of the particle, as should be expected, considering the dichroism data obtained for RNA. A hypothetical arrangement of the tertiary structure consistent with the above evidence, for RNA molecules of moderate ionic strength, was proposed by us in 1960 [12; see also 20, 5, 14, 16]. Two possible variants of the actual arrangement of helices, based on the proposed concepts of the tertiary structure, are shown schematically in Fig. 1. In considering this schematic presentation it should be kept in mind that no fixed position is assumed for any helical region with respect to the neighboring helical areas. The only point stressed in the diagram is that the helical areas are arranged at right angles relative to the long axis of the particle. In the plane perpendicular to the long axis of the particle, the axes of the various helical regions appear to be oriented at random in all directions, following a statistical distribution over the entire 360° range with respect to the long axis of the particle.

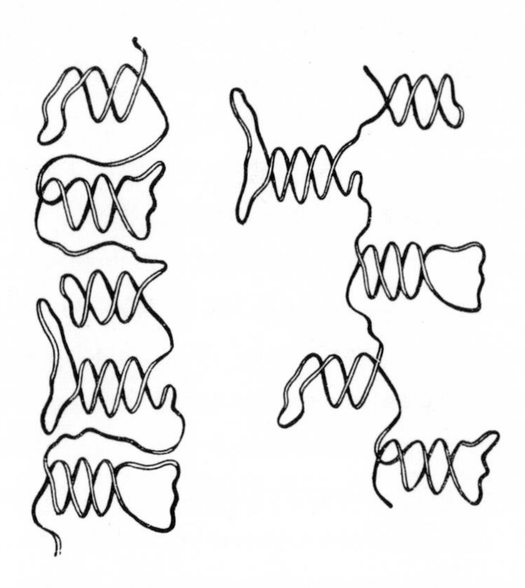

Fig. 1. Schematic presentation of a plausible tertiary structure of RNA, with helical areas arranged at right angles to the long axis of the particle (fragment). Two possible variants.

Such an arrangement of the helical areas in the RNA molecule imposes certain additional requirements with regard to its structural organization. It also leads to two important conclusions concerning the conformation of RNA in solution. The first conclusion is that the type of structure described tentatively in Fig. 1 is not feasible unless the helical regions involved form largely as a result of paired interaction of *adjacent* (neighboring) sections in a single-stranded polynucleotide chain. Fresco, Alberts and Doty [44], starting from entirely different premises, concluded likewise that "... the most stable helical regions emerge due to interaction between adjacent sections of the polyribonucleotide chain."* "Entropy considerations suggest that interactions between distant sections are unlikely, since they would lead to very highly restrictive conformations. Thus, the helical regions take the form of hairpin turns which require a minimum of three unbonded nucleotides to connect the antiparallel hydrogen-bonded chain sections" [44]. Either one or the other variant tentatively proposed for the structural arrangement of helices (Fig. 1) should also be arrived at if the above conclusion were to be applied, unqualifiedly, to the case of high-polymeric RNA containing a large number of helical regions and if some electrostatic repulsion were assumed to exist between such areas.

The second important conclusion is that if the helical areas are arranged in sequence as shown in Fig. 1 (i.e., "stacked up" one on top of another) and if a sufficient number of helical areas are involved (as in the case of high-polymeric RNA), the particle as a whole will tend to assume the shape of a rod. Where the ionic strength is not high so that electrostatic repulsion is still sufficiently pronounced, a large number of hairpin-shaped helical loops (helical areas) will form radiating in all directions from the long axis (Fig. 1, especially the right-hand variant). This in itself will lead to mutual repulsion of such helical areas along the entire length of the particle. In consequence, these areas will be oriented

*Again, as requested by Mr. Spirin, the quotation was not translated but was copied from the original English report [44].—Tr.

in parallel planes, and the particle as a whole will assume the shape of a rod subjected to electrostatic stresses. The structure will thus be held together solely by forces of electrostatic repulsion, which will subject the particle to some tensile stresses, within the covalent framework linking consecutively the individual helical areas. Another structural factor of some importance to be considered involves the metal-complex bridges and nonspecific hydrogen bonds present in the RNA macromolecule. On this basis, some type of bond formation can be assumed to develop between neighboring helical areas. The resulting structure will be similar to the one represented by the left-hand variant in Fig. 1. Extensive evidence has, in fact, been obtained in independent experiments, for the case of relatively low ionic strength, that the molecules of high-polymeric RNA in solution have a rod-shaped conformation.

The proposed concepts of tertiary structure relate to high-polymeric RNA in solutions of moderately high ionic strength, kept at room temperature. To sum up, it can be said that the axes of short bihelical areas, in the form of "hairpin turns," found in the RNA molecule tend to orient themselves predominantly in parallel planes. The helical areas are "stacked up," alternating with some unordered regions. As a result of such structural arrangement, the particle* assumes the shape of a rod.

It will be borne in mind that the structural characteristics depicted in Fig. 1 appear to be specific primarily for the particular case of relatively low ionic forces. This applies both to the orientation of helices with respect to the long axis of the molecule and

*The basic arrangement of helical areas in an RNA molecule, as described, is to be considered principally, if not exclusively, for the case of a high-polymeric molecule. It is hard to believe that a specific regularity pattern may govern the arrangement of helical areas in the "soluble" RNA molecule, which contains not more than 70-90 nucleotides, and most likely develops one, two or, at the most, three helical regions [44].

the rod-shaped conformation assumed by the molecule of high-polymeric RNA. With an increase in ionic strength, the degree of repulsion between the helices will diminish. As a consequence, the particle can be expected to develop a tendency toward additional coiling, with subsequent disorientation of the helices. It follows that even in the case where high ionic forces are present, the coil formation can be assumed to result from "overcoiling" of the long rod, rather than from the single-threaded polynucleotide chain itself being twisted. The tertiary structure remains basically unaltered, but becomes complicated through additional cross-linkages, bends and twists, which hinder direct observation of the original simple regularities governing the orientation of the molecular links. The concept in which coils formed following an increase in ionic strength are visualized as tightly coiled rods is consistent with the conclusions of Fresco and co-workers [44], who believed that conformations of maximum stability form largely through interaction between the adjacent sections (helical regions in the form of hairpin turns) of the chain. Needless to say, between a typical rod-shaped and a typical coil-shaped conformation lies a vast variety of intermediate macromolecular structures, which differ in the degree of "coiling" and spatial asymmetry.

4. TRANSITIONAL CONFORMATIONS

The evidence presented warrants the conclusion that the shape of RNA molecules in solution is determined by the actual conditions existing therein. If the solution is of relatively low ionic strength, the molecules of high-polymeric RNA can be said to have the shape of rods. When acted upon by relatively high ionic forces, the RNA molecules tend to acquire a shape approaching a coil. The coils may form as a result of a more or less random twisting which alters the shape of the original long rods. Moreover, heating of RNA solutions, as stated earlier, causes a disruption of such compact RNA conformations, followed by transition to a more or less unfolded state, in which the chain loses both its tertiary and secondary structures. The transition was detected in studies on the hydrodynamic behavior of virus RNA when heated [8, 22], and it was confirmed by data on UV dichroism of RNA in a heated state [9] as well as by direct electron microscope observations [10]. An identical picture of thermal unfolding was demonstrated for various ribosomal RNA's by use of the same methods (viscosity, sedimentation, UV dichroism, electron microscopy [5, 11, 13, 24]). It is thus seen that RNA, when heated, acquires what amounts essentially to a new conformation, which can be defined as an unfolded, single-stranded polynucleotide chain. The structural transition was found to be reversible in all cases.

On the strength of cumulative evidence, a hypothesis suggesting the existence of three extreme types of conformations assumed by high-polymeric RNA's, with mutually reversible transitions between them, was advanced by us in 1960 [12, 20]. A relevant schematic presentation is given in Fig. 2.

The concept of reversible transitions between various conformations of RNA macromolecules is based on the fact that RNA particles in solution lack any fixed, stable spatial relations between the individual areas and links of the chain. The three-dimensional structure of the RNA molecule contains no covalent bridges able to "cross-link" and thus fix the spatial pattern of the molecule (as will occur in the case of the disulfide bonds in protein molecules). Strong, cooperative, practically irreversible bonding resulting from continuous complementary interaction between polynucleotide sections of considerable length (such as is involved in the specific pairing of two DNA chains) fails to develop in the RNA structure. Such interactions as take place between the individual groups and separate areas in the RNA molecule are labile and reversible. Therefore, the three-dimensional structure

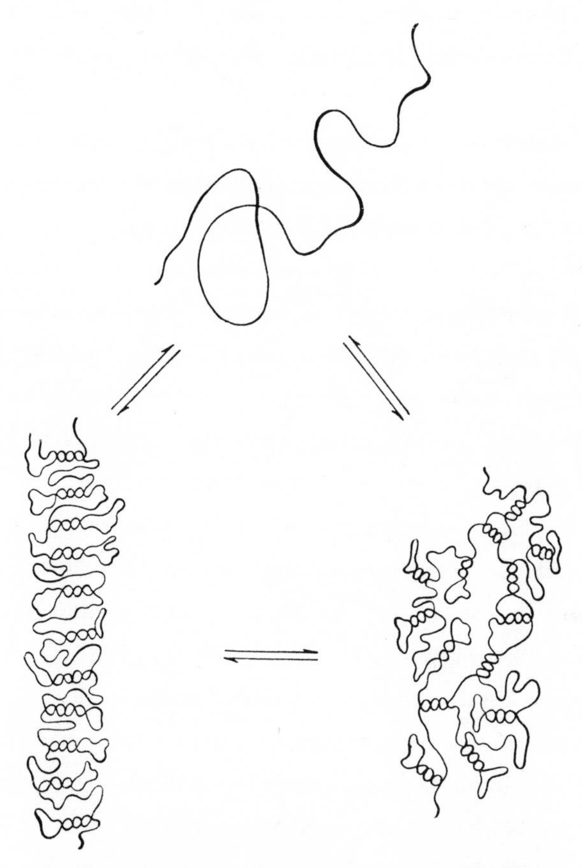

Fig. 2. Schematic presentation of conformations and transitional conformations assumed by the macromolecules of RNA in solution depending on its ionic strength, temperature and the pH ("coil-rod-unfolded strand").

of an RNA molecule is not rigid or fixed, but is mobile, flexible and capable of far-reaching reversible modifications. It is shaped by the hydrogen bonds, by hydrophobic interaction of the bases and possibly, to some extent, by the metal-complex bridges. A further shaping influence is the powerful electrostatic repulsion between the phosphate groups carrying like charges. When equilibrium is attained between these two groups of mutually opposing intramolecular forces, some kind of "pattern" becomes established in the three-dimensional structure of the RNA molecule in solution, within its continuous, linear, flexible covalent framework. Any change in conditions existing in the solution which affects interaction between the RNA molecule and the solvent will displace the equilibrium, and the conformation will be altered in a way reflecting the shift. Thus, any actual conformation assumed by the RNA in solution represents a state of equilibrium existing between the intramolecular forces, on the one hand, and between the molecule and the solvent, on the other, under a given set of actual conditions. It is basically this equilibrium between antagonistic forces that determines the degree of chain spiralization as well as the extent of spatial asymmetry and compactness of the particle. A specified salt concentration of the solution provides a sufficient screening of the negatively charged phosphate groups so that the forces of hydrogen bonding and hydrophobic interaction are far stronger than those of electrostatic repulsion existing under such conditions. The result is a compact conformation saturated with helical regions. Raising the ionic strength leads to additional screening of the phosphate groups, hence to further diminution of electrostatic repulsion in the macromolecule. This, in turn, causes the emergence of some more hydrogen bonds and helical areas. Lowering the ionic strength produces an opposite effect, reaching a point where the chain becomes completely unfolded. What happens is that as the electrostatic repulsion begins to exceed the intramolecular bonding forces, it causes a rupture of the bonds and straightens the chain, by creating some tensile stresses in it. The unfolding of the chain can be facilitated also by loosening the molecular structure in another way, through addition of urea, formamide or dimethylsulfoxide, which will directly affect the intramolecular hydrogen bonds and hydrophobic interaction, weakening both. Heating the solution leads to a thermal rupture of the noncovalent intramolecular linkages, so that the chain again unfolds into a more or less loose structure. In each case, a free, reversible interaction of the chain links leads to the emergence of some definite, stable RNA conformation, most advantageous in terms of energy conservation under the given conditions. This capacity for selective adjustment makes a broad spectrum of conformations available to the RNA molecule, so that to any given set of actual conditions will correspond a single, specific and unique conformation or a set of conformations. Whenever these conditions are altered, the structure will be modified accordingly. If the original conditions are restored, the structure will resume the respective initial conformation.

Chapter III

THE PRINCIPLE OF "INDUCED" CONFORMATIONS IN MACROMOLECULAR BEHAVIOR

1. RNA

Studies of high-polymeric RNA's suggest the necessity of reevaluating the basic concept of the macromolecular structure. Some generally accepted terms, such as "native conformation," "native state," or "tertiary structure," must be redefined for the sake of clarity.

The RNA structure has brought into sharp relief a fact to which little attention has been paid in research work concerned with other biological macromolecules, including those of proteins and DNA. The RNA molecules have been found to lack a permanent, rigidly predetermined, unalterable and highly specific structure, for which a clearly defined mutual arrangement of all the atoms and groups could be described. The RNA structure is fixed *linearly* by its covalent bonds, but its spatial three-dimensional pattern is not fixed. The spatial pattern of this polymer takes shape depending on the equilibrium of some noncovalent, relatively weak forces interacting under any given set of conditions. If the equilibrium is displaced, the actual conformation pattern will be altered. It follows that, theoretically, the molecule can assume any one of a broad spectrum of possible conformations, and that any actual environment will bring about its own type of conformation. Thus, the RNA structure as such possesses an inherent capacity for *responding precisely* to the totality of physical and chemical factors operating in the medium, by altering its conformation. This concept provides an entirely new basis for studying the biological functions of RNA molecules. The existence of a *flexible, induced conformation,* rather than a rigidly fixed one, may prove a decisive factor in the behavior and functioning of cellular RNA's.

From the principle of induced conformations two properties can be inferred which merit the closest scrutiny, since they may determine the nature of functions and the functional mechanism of RNA molecules. The first inference is that every aspect of an RNA conformation is easily *controlled* by various physical and chemical factors. The second conclusion presumes the conformation to be *mobile* while the molecular functioning is in progress.

The possibility that the molecules of cell RNA's may assume induced conformations was discussed for the particular case of biologically active, infectious TMV RNA in an earlier report published by the author in collaboration with L. P. Gavrilova [20]. I shall quote the relevant passages, if I may, practically word for word. We began by stating that the secondary and tertiary structures characteristic for isolated virus RNA in solution are completely absent from the same RNA as it is found in the virus particle. Deproteinization of the virus frees the RNA from its previous protein environment, facilitating interaction between the individual links and sections of the chain, and thus it drastically alters the configuration possessed by the chain while confined in the virus. When transferred to an aqueous solution, the chain coils, forming a compact macromolecule. It is this particular macromolecule, with its subsequently developed secondary and tertiary structures, that is studied in experimenting with "the macromolecule of infectious RNA obtained from the tobacco mosaic virus." Consequently, the secondary and tertiary RNA structures of infectious RNA in solution cannot be identified as some specific, fixed native structures but are simply the result of a free, spontaneous coiling of the chain. The compact particle formed possesses a distinct new conformation, whose uniqueness and specificity is determined by two factors. One involves the possibilities for coiling and spiralization, which depend on the nucleotide sequence as such; the other is associated with the equilibrium established both inside and outside the molecule, i.e., between the intramolecular forces and between the polynucleotide and the solvent. It follows that the newly formed secondary and tertiary structures of an isolated virus RNA can be equated simply with some state of the chain which is most advantageous, under any given conditions, in terms of energy conservation. Yet, the isolated virus RNA fully retains the specificity of biological activity (infectity) it possesses as a native virus component.

It was further pointed out that changes in conditions existing in the solution and the resulting changes in the conformation of virus RNA *in vitro* do not affect the biological, infectious activity of this RNA. In some of our experiments, leaves were infected with RNA dissolved in a 6*M* urea solution. The RNA macromolecules, in this medium, were characterized by a considerable number of ruptured hydrogen bonds, a diminished number of helices, and a somewhat looser state of the particle as a whole, by comparison with macromolecules in the commonly used phosphate buffer.

Nevertheless, the infectious activity level in these preparations was the same as noted for RNA solutions in a phosphate buffer. H. Boedtker [29] infected plants with virus RNA solutions of different ionic strength. The macromolecules, in such solutions, varied accordingly in both shape and degree of spatial asymmetry, yet infectious activity was found to be identical in all cases. In researches conducted at the Fraenkel-Conrat laboratory [51], RNA was injected into plant leaves under conditions where the acid took on the form of an unfolded chain containing no hydrogen bonds or helices (the RNA preparation was first demineralized and then dissolved in distilled water). Even in this case, however, the infectivity of the tested RNA preparation was not in any way affected as compared with RNA's having a "coiled" configuration. It follows that no change involving the secondary or tertiary structure will alter the biological activity of infectious RNA's.

To account for the above experimental results we offered three possible interpretations [20], each based on the assumption that RNA conformations are flexible and capable of undergoing reversible, induced modifications.

(1) The conformation (secondary and tertiary structure) of virus RNA is an essential factor influencing its biological activity. This refers to the actual form assumed by RNA in solutions wherein the pH, ionic strength and temperature are maintained more or less within the "physiological" range. According to all available data, however, changes in conformation produced by altering conditions existing in the solution were found to be reversible in every experiment conducted *in vitro*. Any change in the RNA conformation should therefore be eliminated as soon as the solution is injected into the leaf, since in the cells of a leaf this virus RNA is exposed to some definite, and more or less permanent conditions

involving the pH, ionic strength and temperature. It follows that, irrespective of what particular type of RNA solution is injected into the leaf, the acid will assume a conformation corresponding to such conditions as exist in the leaf cells. The same thing can happen, obviously, in the case of a native virus infection, when the protein membrane of the virus is shed and the RNA, now in a free state, is released into the cell juice of the host. It is possible that an ability to assume a distinct conformation when in solution is indispensable for further participation by the RNA in the infective process. In other words, the biological activity of infectious RNA in solution depends, in addition to its particular nucleotide sequence, on the existence of a balanced three-dimensional molecular structure.

(2) The virus RNA, as it enters the cell of the host, becomes fixed on some cell structures. Under their action the acid, irrespective of the state it was in when used for inoculation, assumes a unique conformation which may have nothing in common with the typical conformations of RNA's in solution, i.e., tested *in vitro*. Inasmuch as RNA's, in general, have an inherent capacity for undergoing a broad variety of induced changes in conformation, it is indeed quite probable that this is what actually takes place in the process of virus infection. The RNA, freed from the protein that previously imparted to it the configuration of a macrohelix, now interacts with certain proteins and structural elements of the cell. As a result, the acid acquires a specific new conformation which provides the necessary basis for biological acitivity manifestations.

(3) The one essential condition for the biological activity of virus RNA is that the nucleotide sequence in the chain (primary structure) remain intact and specific. Any type of secondary or

tertiary structure that may be developed by the chain is of no significance. This assumption will not appear unsound if we recall that unlike certain other compounds, such as proteins, the virus RNA does not appear to function through some spatial active centers. More likely, it serves as a template for reconstructing itself as well as for synthesizing the virus protein. It is by no means implausible, therefore, that the active, functioning state of an RNA molecule within the cell could be identified with a stretched-out chain (or working areas in the chain) containing neither secondary nor tertiary structures.

It can readily be seen that these three possibilities, as discussed, are in no sense mutually exclusive but, on the contrary, complement one another, since each may actually be associated with some stage in the development of infection.

An attempt can thus be made to study and interpret the biological functions of the various RNA's in relation to the principle of induced conformations. Such an approach seems to us both extremely attractive and rich in possibilities. A most readily accessible object for such studies might be found in the ''soluble'' RNA. The molecules of this acid consist of a relatively short polynucleotide chain (not more than 100 nucleotides), and their functions are most clearly defined. In their macrostructure, these molecules appear to be far less complex than those of high-polymeric RNA. In many other respects, they are the most thoroughly explored of the various RNA molecules. Several years ago Brown and Zubay [34] reported that preparations of free ''soluble'' RNA were found to differ from those of ''soluble'' RNA combined with amino acids in a number of physicochemical characteristics, such as the rate of sedimentation in an ultracentrifuge. This suggested that the linking of an amino acid to the end adenosine in the chain of "soluble" RNA must have caused a distinct change in the conformation of the RNA molecule. Quite recently, on the other hand, Tissieres et al. [68] showed that the "soluble" RNA's are a strong specific inhibitor of the RNA-polymerase reaction (an enzymic system synthesizing messenger RNA from nucleoside triphosphates, on a DNA template), whereas "soluble" RNA's combined with amino acids exhibit no such activity. The biological significance of this observation is rather obvious. If the cell does not contain a sufficient amount of amino acids, i.e., material from which the proteins must be built, the "soluble" RNA's will be in a free state, with no amino acids attached. They will thus inhibit the synthesis of messenger RNA, no longer needed, since protein synthesis is not possible. Most likely, it seems, this regulating effect of the "soluble" RNA is based on induced changes in its molecular conformation. Specifically, the linking of amino acids to the end of the "soluble" RNA chain alters its conformation in solution, and the resulting new conformation no longer exhibits any inhibitory effect on the RNA-polymerase system. The possibility that the "soluble" RNA molecules may exist in various induced states seems to warrant a special study. The results of such research might prove an invaluable contribution to our inquiry into the many still little understood aspects of protein synthesis in the cell.

The point I should particularly like to stress is the importance of induced conformations as a basic concept to be considered in discussing the interaction of various RNA's involved in protein synthesis taking place in the ribosome. Complementary interaction between some area of one RNA molecule and the respective area of another RNA molecule is bound to cause certain rearrangements in the conformations of both molecules. What is meant by complementary interaction, it will be recalled, is not an ordinary adhesion of two small immobile surface areas of the molecules but a spiralization and mutual coiling of chain sections. This cannot but alter the respective conformations to a lesser or greater extent, at least along the regions of the two molecules adjacent to each other. Moreover, a chain section in one molecule may be freed from an intramolecular helical region already formed and become involved in a complementary interaction with another molecule. This will occur if, of the two competing combinations, interaction with a chain area in another molecule is more advantageous, in terms of energy conservation, than interaction of the two chain sections confined to one and the same molecule. Changes affecting the conformations, in this case, can be expected to prove even more marked. What goes on in the ribosome may evidently include a complex pattern of interactions between various RNA's. Template (messenger) RNA, as it is fixed on the ribosome, appears to become linked simultaneously to the ribosomal subunits, presumably through complementary interaction between some of its chain sections and those of ribosomal RNA's. In all likelihood, this applies also to the binding of "soluble" RNA in the ribosome particle. The "soluble" RNA is, furthermore, an adaptor and, as such, will interact with template RNA in the course of protein synthesis. The special task of the two ribosomal RNA molecules in the ribosome may consist in binding template and adaptor RNA's, whereby their fixed, strictly determined orientation is ensured both relative to each other and with respect to the polypeptide chain being formed. Simultaneous binding at several (a minimum of two) points imparts rigidity to such orientation. Quite obviously, the coding nucleotide combinations on the template and adaptor could not locate one another, nor could each successive amino acid contact the end of the polypeptide chain being built, without a rigid mutual orientation of all the links involved in protein synthesis. But ribosomal RNA may have another important function, besides maintaining the orientation and the rigid mutual spatial arrangement of the various RNA's at any given time in the course of protein synthesis. Its most essential task is, perhaps, to control the proper sequence of events throughout this process. The assumption is a tempting one. Such a succession of events, according to currently available data [47, 61], can be visualized as follows. Each time the formation of another peptide bond is completed, an opportunity is afforded thereby for the "readout" of the next coding combination on the template. As a result, another "soluble" RNA molecule, corresponding to the particular combination, becomes bound by the ribosome with the attached amino acid. This in turn leads to the formation of a new peptide bond between the C-end of the polypeptide in the process of buildup and the NH_2 group of the amino acid linked to the "soluble" RNA. (The latter, therefore, remains linked to the new polypeptide being formed.) Simultaneously, the "soluble" RNA that brought in the preceding amino acid splits off and leaves the ribosome. The cycle is then repeated.

It can be assumed, in a most general way, that the sequence of events in protein synthesis is determined by successive cyclic changes in the ribosomal RNA conformation, resulting from complementary interaction between some of its chain sections and those of messenger RNA as well as the "soluble" RNA's.

2. THE PROTEINS

As we consider the RNA structure with its biologically significant implications, we must pause to ponder a point. Are flexibility and mobility of the macromolecular structure restricted to this class of biological macromolecules alone? Perhaps similar potentialities with respect to flexibility and induced changes are inherent in the structure of linear biological polymers of another type, such as the proteins? Could the functional mechanisms of, say, the enzymic proteins be understood if these were regarded as rigidly fixed structures, not much different, basically, from the usual type of catalysts?

The historically established, classic approach to protein structure has in many ways been associated with advances in chemical research on this group of native compounds. The chemists are used to dealing with definite, stable molecular conformations. If we consider that for many years the study of protein structure has been almost exclusively in their province, the tendency to apply the classic propositions of chemistry to protein compounds will appear perfectly natural.

From such an approach to the protein problem evolved the "lock and key" theory of Fischer, which has won universal recognition and is considered practically an axiom. The concept purports to explain the specificity of the catalytic action displayed by enzymes. The basic proposition of this theory holds that the protein-enzyme has a rigid fixed active center whose conformation is the "negative" of the substrate conformation. Specificity is the result of steric correspondence between the active center and the substrate. Later on, thanks to outstanding advances in the X-ray analysis of proteins achieved in the past decade, a three-dimensional structure was established for some crystalline proteins. This structure, which undoubtedly corresponds to the state of the conformation actually assumed by the protein molecule in the crystal, came to be regarded as a fixed, specific "tertiary structure," generally inherent in a given protein.

With all that, it has long been known that protein molecules will undergo reversible as well as irreversible changes in conformation and biological (enzymic) activity induced by various factors affecting intramolecular interactions or interactions of the molecules with the solvent (temperature, pH, ionic strength, polarity of solvent, the presence of chemical agents such as urea, etc.). The changes may be either abrupt, stepwise ones or relatively mild and gradual ones. Drastic, stepwise structural changes associated with inactivation, mostly irreversible or partially reversible, are usually referred to as "denaturation" of the protein molecule.

"Denaturation" in this case implies merely that a protein polypeptide chain, unlike that of RNA, can exist in more than one, relatively stable, state under any given set of actual conditions. The relative stability means that certain energy barriers separate these states. One such state, which is characteristic for a given protein in the cell, and in which the protein exhibits a biologic activity, is called the native state; the others are denatured states. A protein molecule in its native state is in turn characterized by a wide spectrum of closely related conformations with practically no energy barriers between them, rather than by a single, clearly defined and permanent conformation. In other words, within the limits of a native state, some very distinct, gradual and freely reversible changes in conformation may occur depending on variable conditions existing in the solution. Under any given set of stable conditions, moreover, some scattering of kindred conformations may take place, with some occasional fluctuations between them.

Conditions under which smooth, reversible changes in the enzymic activity of proteins are possible, depending on temperature, pH, ionic strength, the presence of urea, composition of solvent, have been widely explored for a very large number of enzymes.

True, in most instances an attempt was made to relate all such activity variations to a direct effect of various influencing factors on the chemical groupings present in the active center (ionizing certain groups or inhibiting their dissociation, specific binding of some particular ion, etc.), even though such an explanation might prove inadequate in many cases. It can hardly be doubted that very often, if not always, activity variations are associated also with changes in conformation within the active center or the macromolecule as a whole. This is especially true for cases involving the effect of urea, solvent polarity, or a reversible temperature effect.

Direct data on smooth, reversible changes in conformation obtained for protein molecules in solution were reported some time ago by D. L. Talmud and co-workers [25]. Their experiments showed that the spatial asymmetry of the protein globule is reduced following addition of dehydrating substances to the solution, which lower the energy of interaction between the hydrophilic groups of the protein and the solvent. Urea, guanidine, etc., on the contrary, enhanced the asymmetry of the particles. In keeping with their experiments, the authors advanced a theory of protein structure in which the protein particle, as a basic proposition, was assumed to represent an equilibrium pattern between mutually opposing forces. Two groups of antagonistic forces are involved: those of interaction between hydrophobic radicals in the amino acid residues, which tend to twist the polypeptide chain into a globule, and those of interaction between hydrophilic radicals and the solvent, which tend to stretch the globule. The protein globule was thus conceived of as a flexible structure capable of undergoing smooth reversible changes. One can fully subscribe to the opinion voiced by S. E. Bresler, V. P. Kushner and S. Ya. Frenkel [6] that although the proposed model of the protein macromolecule has been materially altered since that time, the basic concepts have retained their significance to this day. It was demonstrated by these authors, at the current level of our understanding of protein structure, that when the composition of the solvent is altered gradually (through partial replacement of water by organic solvents of low polarity such as dioxane or ethylene chlorohydrin), a large number of proteins undergo equally smooth changes in the degree of helicity and spatial asymmetry of their molecules, i.e., nondenaturing modifications of the secondary and tertiary structures [6].

Further data on possible occurrence of smooth and completely reversible changes in conformation depending on the composition of solvent were reported by the Doty laboratory [39]. On the basis of these results, Doty wrote:* "Then, it would appear that the helical content of proteins is a result of balance between the intramolecular hydrogen bonding of the protein and the hydrogen-bonding capacity of the solvent. When water is the solvent, the point of balance is in many cases near 50% [e.g., about 50% of the molecular structure has assumed the configuration of an α-helix] and *can be shifted in either direction by proper alteration of the solvent*" [39]. (The italics are mine: A. S.)

Of decisive importance were the discovery and subsequent studies of the so-called allosteric effects. In recent years these investigations have lent powerful support to the concept of the protein molecule as a flexible structure capable of undergoing reversible induced changes in conformation. In the same research, a direct relationship has been established between this property of

*The cited passage was again copied from Doty's original paper, but the statement in the square brackets does *not* appear in the original text (it must have been inserted by Mr. Spirin for clarity).—Tr.

proteins and their biological functions. Manifestations of allosteric effects were first detected in experiments where the *end product* in a chain of consecutive biochemical reactions (usually, those of biosynthesis) was found to be a specific inhibitor of the enzyme that had catalyzed the initial reaction in this chain ("end-product inhibition" or "feedback inhibition") [70]. In other words, if we have a chain of transformations

$$A \xrightarrow{E_1} B \xrightarrow{E_2} C \xrightarrow{E_3} D \xrightarrow{E_4} E \xrightarrow{E_5} F$$

and if each reaction in the chain is catalyzed by its own enzyme (E_1, E_2, E_3, E_4, E_5), then the end product F is an inhibitor of enzyme E_1, i.e., of the enzyme catalyzing the initial link of the chain, *even though F is no longer a steric analog of substrate A.* This has been found to hold for the majority of biosynthetic chain reactions. In the case considered above, the inhibitor did not in any way affect directly the active center of the enzyme. For this reason it was named an "allosteric inhibitor," to distinguish it from the usual "isosteric inhibitors" which act upon the active center, because of their structural likeness to the substrate [62]. In the case under consideration, the enzyme (E_1) was found to have a special area, distinct from the active center of catalysis, where the particular "allosteric" inhibitor (F) could be attached to it [35, 45]. Analysis of available data led to the conclusion that "the action of allosteric inhibitors is not due to a direct interference by steric hindrance, but rather to an induced alteration of the shape or structure of the enzyme protein, resulting in misfit or reduced fit of the substrate at the active site"* [54].

It has been found, at the same time, that allosteric effects are not limited to allosteric inhibition but can be positive as well; i.e.,

---

*Copied from the original report.—Tr.

following interaction of the enzyme with some substance (allosteric effector), the affinity between the active center and the substrate may become enhanced, resulting in activation of the enzyme. Thus, while isoleucine allosterically inhibits threonine desaminase [35], valine activates it [36]. In a similar case of aspartic transcarbamylase, CTP acts as an allosteric inhibitor of the enzyme, while ATP allosterically activates it [45]. In a recent report, F. Jacob and J. Monod [54] commented on the work of Traut concerned with glycogen synthetase from animal tissues, which catalyzes the synthesis of glycogen from uridine-diphosphate-glucose. It was found that the enzyme is strongly activated by glucose-1-phosphate and is inhibited by ATP. Neither effect could be attributed to direct action upon the active center, but both were shown to be associated with a specific linkage to another area of the protein molecule and, in consequence, with *an induced structural change in the protein itself.* Some interesting data were also obtained by Tomkins and Yielding [69] who showed that in the presence of some steroids, the enzyme glutamic dehydrogenase becomes inactive with respect to glutamic acid, but acquires activity with regard to alanine. The transition involves some structural changes (dissociation) in the molecules of this protein-enzyme.

Thus, from the limited data available at this time, it is evident that the protein molecules have a distinct capacity for undergoing induced modifications of their native structure. Such structural (conformational) changes are induced when certain substances become attached to specific areas in the protein molecules, situated outside the active center. An induced change in conformation also affects the active center of the protein, with the result that its biological activity is altered, through inhibition, activation, or modified specificity of the catalyzing action. It follows that flexibility and mobility of conformation enable the protein molecule to respond adequately to such influencing factors as may be associated with the medium—which is tantamount to a capacity for being controlled by these factors. In the light of such evidence, the protein molecule can be visualized as a system that has only one "outlet," a catalyzing active center, and a few (or many) "inlets," or pickup centers for receiving various "chemical signals" such as the allosteric effectors. That is why the protein molecule should scarcely be approached as a mere skeleton structure, or a high-molecular-weight carrier, for the catalyzing active center. The part of a protein molecule outside the active center is designed, most likely, to function as a highly specific receiver and conversion transducer of the numerous "signals" (either physical factors or chemical substances) which control protein activity in the cell, as well as the functional state of its active center. Flexible geometry and the capacity for undergoing induced structural modifications are the two properties that account for such "controllability" of functional activity exhibited by the proteins.

Finally, in the light of new ideas in enzymology, still awaiting general acknowledgment, new trends and supporting data, the mobility of protein structure emerges as a basic factor of major importance. Not only does it *control* the catalyzing activity of proteins, but it is directly involved in the *implementation of the process of catalysis itself.* First to be mentioned in this connection is a new theory of the action and specificity of enzymes proposed and developed by D. E. Koshland [56-59]. The classic lock-and-key theory of Fischer, predicated on a rigid spatial steric conformity between substrate and the active center, was actually sufficient to explain in a simple and logical fashion the broad evidence of the strict specificity and selectivity of enzymic action. Because the theory worked, it seemed attractive, to a point where it has now become a generally accepted axiom. Koshland, however, has pointed out a large number of anomalous cases, difficult to explain, which somehow did not fit the proposed generalized concepts. Fischer's theory, for example, offered an adequate explanation for those cases where the analogs of a substrate, exceeding the latter in their molecular dimensions, failed to react with the active center of the enzyme, even though they possessed all the necessary groupings, in the proper positions, for being linked to this center. It was clear that the molecules of such analogs were simply too large for "squeezing" into the rigid pattern of the active center. But what about the cases where analogs with smaller molecules as compared with the substrate have likewise failed to react with the active center of the enzyme? This could not very well be explained as above. Among other instances, Koshland considers the hexokinase reaction. It proved rather difficult to explain, in this case, why water will not react with ATP, either in the presence or in the absence of glucose, while glucose does react with it. To explain such anomalies a new theory of the specificity of enzymic action was proposed, the so-called "induced-fit theory" [56-59], in which protein molecules are assumed to have a flexible conformation. The protein-enzyme, according to this concept, exists in some conformation that is natural for the given conditions. Its potential active center, furthermore, is not necessarily a negative of the substrate, i.e., it may lack any steric conformity with it. "Substrate interaction produces a new protein geometry, perhaps in a way similar to that in which urea affects the shape of restricted portions of a protein molecule" [58]. The induced change in conformation leads to an appropriate spatial arrangement of the catalyzing groups in the potential active center, so that the proper reaction becomes catalyzed. As the reaction products are released from the surface of the enzyme, the active center reverts to its original conformation. In some instances the action needed to attain a correct arrangement of the catalyzing groups in the enzyme will not come directly from those groupings in the substrate which are linked to the active center or participate in the reaction, but rather from some attendant groupings, with molecules of a certain size. This explains why the analogs sometimes fail to participate in the enzymic reaction, even when their molecules are smaller than those of the substrate (as in the case of water in the hexokinase reaction). The entire sequence of events involved in the enzymic action (interaction with substrate—induced change in conformation—release of reaction products—return to the original conformation—followed by repetition of the cycle) signifies that the protein-enzyme does not function as a fixed, permanently set catalyzing surface but rather as an *active* mechanism "working" in cycles.

3. SOME GENERAL CONCLUSIONS

What has been said above reflects, it would seem, a qualitatively new approach to the essential macromolecular structure of biopolymers. Studies of biological macromolecules, especially those concerned with the proteins and nucleic acids, make us increasingly aware of the narrowness of our diehard conventionalized concepts. We still visualize a unique, unalterably predetermined tertiary structure, an active center having a fixed conformation; a spatial "pattern" in the polymer arrangement depending on a single set of factors; the extent of spiralization inherent in the structure, etc. It is possible that for the biopolymers *in vivo* all this exists in a far less rigorously determined form than is customarily envisioned on the basis of the classic chemical studies and structural X-ray analysis. The most important, functionally active biopolymers—proteins and nucleic acids—may be characterized by a broad continuous, or discontinuous, spectrum of induced conformations. Needless to say, in each case there exist some definite and specific boundaries or limits which truly characterize the biopolymer in its native state. Changes in conformation, under physiological conditions, do not extend beyond these limits. It would seem useful, in this sense, to preserve such concepts as tertiary structure, active center conformation, degree of helicity, etc., provided it is understood that what is meant is not rigorously delimited "single-point" states but, rather, a broad range or region of states within which a natural scattering is possible or has been actually shown to exist. This new approach, which in recent years has been steadily gaining ground, makes us more keenly aware than every before of the significance of biopolymers in the biologic organization as a whole. The purely structural basic concept of induced conformations harbors some highly important rudimentary premises or, to be more precise, a molecular basis for the biological functions. Such preconditions included, first, reactivity, adequate environmental responses, total controllability and, second, mobility in functioning, i.e., intramolecular "movements" performed during the "work" process. Such, it would seem, is the unique behavioral peculiarity, inherent in biologic macromolecules alone, which is the basic point of distinction between these molecules and the ambient abiogenic systems. The latter may model outwardly some aspects of the biological functions, but they are themselves immobile and noncontrollable (as are, say, all nonprotein catalysts).

Chapter IV

THE STRUCTURE, BIOSYNTHESIS AND FUNCTIONING OF RIBOSOMES

The task of determining the true relationship between the macromolecular structure of ribonucleic acids and their biological functions in the cell brings us directly to a problem that lies at the root of modern biology. We must study the molecular mechanisms involved in protein synthesis. We know today that a variety of functionally distinct RNA fractions exist in the cell and that protein synthesis is the end result of complex molecular interactions between these various types of cellular polyribonucleotides. This refers, above all, to ribosomal, template and adaptor RNA's. Our present knowledge of these complex processes is limited to a rather sketchy notion of a complementary interaction between the template (messenger RNA) and adaptor (''soluble'' RNA). We know nothing about the mechanisms controlling the participation in these processes by the active center links of the protein-synthesizing apparatus, i.e., by the ribosome itself and the ribosomal RNA.

It is in the ''apparatus'' of the ribosome that protein synthesis is carried out. The ribosome contains all three known types of cellular RNA, and it is there that they perform their respective functions in the final shaping of the specific polypeptide chain in the protein. It follows that before the molecular mechanisms involved in the functioning of the various RNA's within the cell can be established, we must solve a general problem relating to all these acids. We must know, that is, how the ribosome performs its "work" in the course of protein synthesis. Obviously, the specific functions of the ribosomal, template and adaptor RNA's cannot be understood, nor any actual relationship between their structure and their functions determined, unless the structure and functions of the ribosomes are studied first.

But the ribosome problem is one of wider, more general biologic significance. The ribosomes are universal particles which exist in all organisms, in all types of cells, without exception. Protein synthesis, the pivotal biochemical activity of living matter, is carried on in the ribosomes. Today we cannot think of life, in its contemporary forms, without considering the ribosomes and the biochemical apparatus servicing them. Most striking is the fact that not only the ribosomes themselves but the reactions developing around them as well, are universal. This can mean but one thing: that some paramount principles of biologic organization are inherent in the ribosome structure and, therefore, in the way in which it functions. It might be added that the ribosomes are the smallest known cellular granules and, as such, belong properly on the borderline between the cellular organoids and macromolecules. In any event, they can be studied by any method of macromolecular physical chemistry. Consequently, in this case, as in no other, it can be hoped that some principles of biologic organization will be uncovered in the molecular organization itself of these particles.

As regards their chemical nature, the ribosomes are ribonucleoprotein particles (RNP-particles) consisting of high-polymeric ribosomal RNA plus structural protein. According to the literature data [52, 15], the ribosomes from various organisms contain 40-65% RNA, hence 60-35% protein, based on dry weight. Individual ribosomes obtained from different biological objects range from 2.8-4.5 million in molecular weight, with respective sedimentation coefficients equaling 70-85 Svedberg units. Such ribosomal particles invariably dissociate, forming two unequal subunits, when the Mg^{++} concentration declines to a certain level. Thus, ribosomes from *Escherichia coli*, with a sedimentation coefficient 70 Svedberg units (the so-called 70S particles) dissociate into subunits with respective sedimentation coefficients of 50 and 30 Svedberg units (50S and 30S particles). At higher Mg^{++} ion concentrations, two 70S particles may aggregate into a single 100S particle. Both dissociation and association are reversible. Each subunit (50S and 30S) consists of a single ribosomal RNA molecule whose molecular weight equals 1.2 million for the 50S subunit and 0.5 million for the 30S subunit, plus a few tens of molecules of structural ribosomal protein.

Detailed electron microscope studies of normal ribosomal particles from *E. coli* were carried out by C. E. Hall and H. S. Slayter [50], using the preshadowing technique. H. E. Huxley and G. Zubay [53] conducted similar experiments in which the method of negative and positive contrasting was applied. Recently, an electron microscope analysis of ribosomes from *E. coli* was performed by N. A. Kisselev (Insitute of Crystallography, Academy of Sciences, USSR) in the course of studies on ribosome structure undertaken by our team [23]. Our observations, which were on the whole consistent with the results of earlier research, furnished some additional and more detailed information on the shape of ribosome particles.

The micrograph in Fig. 3a shows the 70S ribosomes from *E. coli* and their dimers, the 100S particles. Each 70S ribosome, whether or not incorporated in a dimer, is seen to be distinctly subdivided into two unequal subunits. One is large and approximately spherical in shape (the 50S subunit), the other is smaller (the 30S subunit) and has a flattened shape, which appears slightly concave on the side adjacent to the larger subunit. The characteristic dimensions, for the group of 70S ribosomes shown in the micrograph, are about 190Å in one direction and up to 160Å in the other. In 70S ribosomes which have undergone dimerization, it is clearly seen that a 100S particle has been formed through interaction of their smaller subunits. Such ribosomal dimers, or 100S particles, measure about 400Å in length and up to 160Å in width.

In the micrographs which show preparations of ribosomes dissociated into the component 50S and 30S subunits, some of the observed structures can be identified as rounded particles about 160Å in diameter. Characteristically, a few of these appear to have a faceted, say, pentagonal configuration. Most likely, they are the 50S subunits. Another type of structure is represented by some rectangular particles noted in the same preparations. In Fig. 3b are shown some areas of micrographs in which the ribosomes are dissociated into 50S and 30S subunits. In micrographs of preshadowed samples (which will not be shown here) the 30S subunits appear as flattened particles 70-90Å in height. Thus, while a 50S particle can be visualized as having a nearly spherical, slightly faceted configuration, a 30S particle should be described as a more or less flattened structure. This holds particularly for cases where it has not been bound with a 50S particle to form a

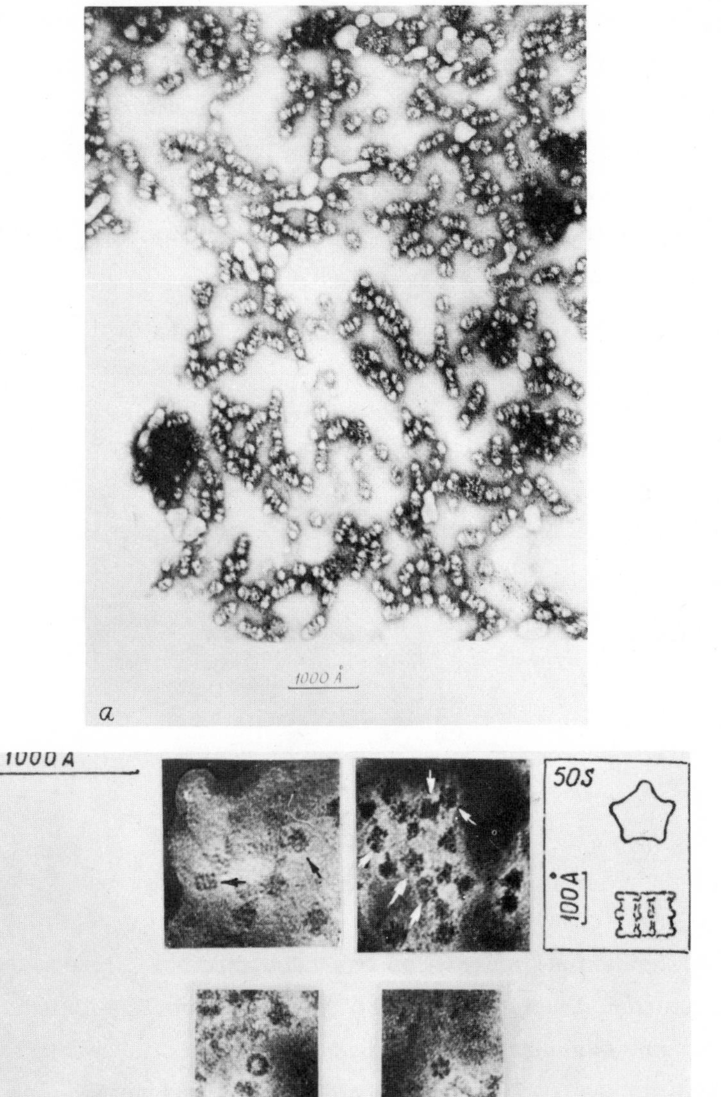

Fig. 3a. Electron micrograph of ribosomes contrasted with PTA: 100S and 70S particles.
Fig. 3b. Electron micrographs of ribosomes contrasted with PTA: 50S and 30S particles; as viewed in projection, these particles have a rectangular or pentagonal, occasionally hexagonal shape.

complete ribosome. Apparently, as a 70S particle is formed, the 30S subunit, while interacting with the 50S subunit, changes its conformation somewhat, assuming the shape of a shallow cup, or a cap, which is fitted over one side of the large subunit.

The morphology and dimensions of ribosomal particles from *E. coli* and of their subunits are shown schematically (Fig. 4) in a presentation based on the above data.

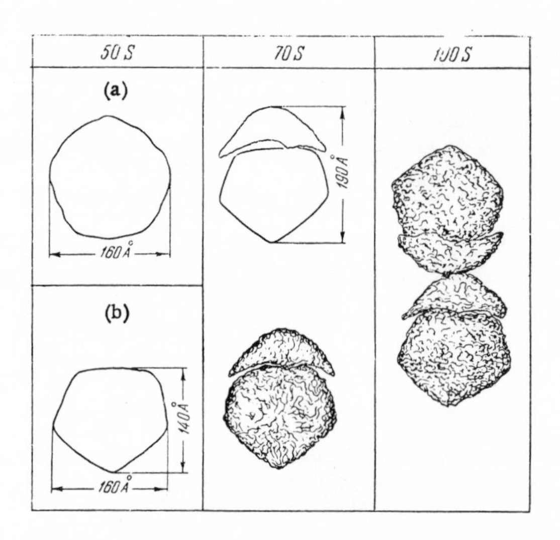

Fig. 4. Dimensions and shape of ribosomal particles from *E. coli* (diagram); (a) top view; (b) side view.

Rather scant information has been made available to date on the internal structural organization of ribosomal particles. Some important evidence was obtained in electron microscope studies of ribosomes contrasted by means of uranyl acetate, which is bonded predominantly by RNA [53]. The experiments failed to disclose any preferential concentration of ribosomal protein or ribosomal RNA in these particles, either on the periphery or in the center. This suggests that protein interlaced with RNA are distributed more or less uniformly through the entire mass of the ribosome. The ribosomal particle is not enveloped by any kind of membrane. This distinguishes it from the virus particles, in which the RNA is concentrated on the inside, forming the nuclein nucleus of the particle, while the protein is spread along the periphery. It is packed densely, forming a membrane which shields the RNA chain from direct contact with the outer medium. Presumably, therefore, the protein molecules accompany the coiled RNA chain along its entire length. The absence of a continuous membrane in ribosomal particles, and the possibility of direct contact between some areas in the RNA and the outer medium, were confirmed also in our experiments testing the effect of exogenous ribonuclease on RNA contained in the ribosomes [26]. It was shown that ribonuclease present in the solution (outer medium) will easily damage the RNA within the ribosome since it affects some areas in the RNA chain which apparently are not shielded by protein. The shape integrity of the particle is, however, not affected in the process ("latent ribosome degradation").

Some information on the state of RNA existing in ribosomes was obtained by structural X-ray analyses [73, 55] as well as in studies of UV hypochromic effect [73, 31, 65]. It was found that the diffraction picture of the ribosomes themselves is practically the same as that obtained by superimposing an X-ray picture of isolated RNA on that of free ribosomal protein. Analysis of X-ray pictures indicated that RNA found in ribosomes is characterized by the presence of helical areas of the same nature and structure as those contained by free RNA in solution. Studies of UV hypochromic effect in ribosomes yielded further evidence that the number of helical areas and the percentage of spiralized nucleotides in RNA within the ribosome are approximately the same as those characteristic for RNA in solutions of moderate ionic strength. The two sets of data seem to warrant the conclusion that the RNA chains in the ribosomes form a large number of double-stranded helical regions, as a result of interaction between sections of the same chain. A secondary structure is thus developed which is similar to that found in free RNA.

It can be seen that the bulk of available information on the ribosomes is largely descriptive in nature. What we have, basically, is a collection of data on some general or specific features of the protein and nuclein components in ribosomes. The information relates to their chemical composition, dimensions, morphology, division into subunits, chemical and physico-chemical properties, etc. On the basis of such evidence alone it is of course difficult to formulate any principles governing the molecular organization of the ribosomes, much less to develop any actual, or hypothetical, model of the ribosome structure. Prompted by these considerations, we undertook a structural study of ribonucleoprotein particles, the ribosomes, based on the experience gained in our earlier researches on the macromolecular structure of high-polymeric RNA in solution. The work was, in fact, a continuation of our previous studies concerned with free ribosomal RNA. Experiments on ribosome structure were begun in our laboratory two years ago and are now carried on in collaboration with N. A. Kisselev (Protein Structure Laboratory, Institute of Crystallography, Academy of Sciences USSR). The actual operations have been carried our largely by co-workers who must be credited with obtaining most of the data to be presented here—among them R. S. Shakulov, member of the laboratory staff; A. A. Bogdanov, Cand. Chem.

Sci., research assistant in training, of the Laboratory of Protein Research, Department of Chemistry, Moscow State University; also, in certain phases of experimentation, M. A. Ajtkhozhin and G. G. Gause, graduate students of Moscow State University working on their theses, as well as Dr. S. Zadražil, research assistant in training, of the Institute of Organic Chemistry and Biochemistry, Czechoslovakian Academy of Sciences (Prague, Czechoslovakian SSR).

Three different approaches have been, and still are, followed in these studies of ribosome structure and of the basic laws governing ribosome formation:

(1) Controlled partial degradiation of ribosomes, as well as other methods of subjecting ribosomal particles in solution to the effect of artificially created influencing factors. This technique aims at inducing possible structural transformations that might disclose the essential organization of ribosomes.

(2) Study of native intracellular ribosome precursors whose structure may constitute a simplified prototype of the ribosomal subunits.

(3) Tentative reconstruction of ribosomal particles outside the cell, *in vitro*.

By combining these fundamental techniques with electron microscope and physicochemical analyses, we have thus far been able to demonstrate that a ribonucleoprotein strand (RNA strand), 30-40Å in diameter, is the structural basis of every ribosomal subunit [23]. It is possible that such a strand is made up from a "rod-shaped" molecule of ribosomal RNA, with a fully developed secondary structure (an assembly of short, double-stranded helical areas). It may further be assumed that the strand is stabilized through interaction of individual RNA sections, which recur at fairly regular intervals, with molecules of ribosomal protein. The ribonucleoprotein strand is coiled in a very specific fashion, forming a compact ribosomal subunit. On the basis of extensive observations a hypothetical model was proposed [23] suggesting a possible arrangement of the RNA strand in a ribosome. A series of intermediate stages was tentatively outlined for ribosome formation in the cell (ribosome biogenesis).

1. EXPERIMENTAL MODIFICATION OF THE RIBOSOME STRUCTURE

The major difficulty in attempting a controlled structural modification of ribosomes in solution is that any kind of action disrupting the native ribosome structure will also activate the latent ribonuclease, a component of the ribosome particle. And this in turn will lead invariably to rapid degradation of the ribosomal RNA and of the entire particle as a whole.

To obviate this difficulty we turned first to formaldehyde, which completely inhibits the enzyme activity and at the same time ensures a firm fixation of the protein structures. The use of formaldehyde as a ribosome fixative, to facilitate electron microscope studies of these particles, was described in an earlier report [53]. It was shown in the same experiments that the visible structure of ribosomal particles is not appreciably altered by fixation. *In vitro* fixation of isolated ribosomes was achieved by incubating them for several hours in the cold in a 4-8% formaldehyde solution. The excess of formaldehyde was then removed from the solution by dialysis. The fixed ribosomes were stable in solution even when magnesium ions were completely absent. They gave normal sedimentation and electron microscope pictures, and showed no sign of ribonuclease activity.

The first encouraging results were obtained when such particles were subjected to the action of urea. On transferring the fixed (''formalimized'') ribosome to a 6*M* urea solution, a decline of sedimentation coefficients (reduced to standard conditions: water, 20°C), varying from one experiment to another but quite substantial, was noted for both ribosomal subunits. (The fixed particles, incidentally, dissociated into these subunits in the presence of urea.) The lowering of sedimentation coefficients was accompanied by an increase in the specific viscosity of the particles, with no separation of any appreciable amount of protein in evidence. The previously compact particles seemed to have been loosened somewhat by the action of urea, without dissociating into RNA and protein. The electron microscope analysis, difficult though it was to carry out in solutions containing high concentrations of urea, indicated that the ribosomal particles had lost their distinct shapes and outlines. Most important, they now showed some spliced ''fibers'' protruding from the ''body'' of the particle. These rod-shaped structures, about 30-40Å in diameter, varied in length but were predominantly short. The appearance of similar ''fibers'' or ''strands'' was noted also in ''formalinized'' ribosomes treated with a detergent, dodecyl sodium sulfate, in small concentrations or exposed to the effect of various other agents. Similar short ''strands'' jutting out of the particle could often be detected in electron microscopy of normal (unfixed) ribosomes. This happened, for example, when the sample had undergone a spontaneous, mild degradation while being prepared or when the ribosomal particles were chromatographed on a column filled with DEAE-cellulose, etc. A typical electron micrograph which shows ribosomal particles with ''fibers'' projecting from them in all directions is given in

Fig. 5. In urea-treated samples the appearance of such short strands was not associated with the splitting off of free protein from the ribosomes. It was thought possible, therefore, that the protrusions were not necessarily identifiable as tips of RNA "rods" extending outside the ribosome but could consist of RNA linked with protein; i.e., their chemical nature could be that of

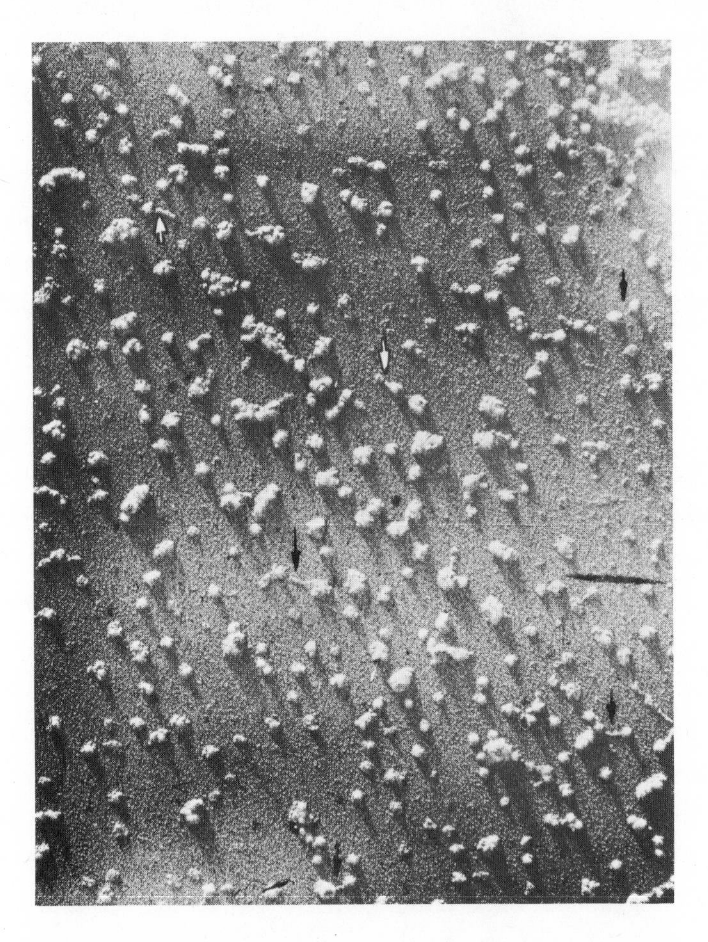

Fig. 5. An electron micrograph of preshadowed ribosomes subjected to partial degradation; short strands protruding from the particles are noted.

ribonucleoprotein. Perhaps the ribosomal particles could be forced with the aid of some agent to unfold completely, forming ribonucleoprotein strands? The possibility seemed well worth verifying.

Attempts to use formaldehyde-fixed ribosomes for this purpose failed, because the fixation resulted apparently in a considerable "cross-linking" of the ribosome, which hindered its complete unfolding. Fortunately, W. Stanley and R. Bock, in a personal communication, informed us of a method for removing the latent ribonuclease from native ribosomes with the aid of $0.5M$ NH_4Cl, without causing any apparent structural and chemical disruptions or alterations of the ribosomal particles. The suggested procedure has been used by us to obtain "ribonuclease-free" ribosomal 50S and 30S subunits.

In these experiments the pure preparations of normal 70S ribosomes were suspended in $0.5M$ NH_4Cl containing $0.001M$ tris buffer, pH 7.8, and the whole was left in the refrigerator for 15 hours. By the end of that time interval, the 70S ribosomes were found to have completely dissociated into the component subunits, which in this solution had sedimentation coefficients of 45 and 30 Svedberg units (45S and 30S). At this point the ribonuclease, according to W. Stanley and R. Bock, is washed from the ribosomes into the solution. To separate coarse impurities and aggregates, the solution containing the ribosomes (45S and 30S) was centrifuged at $20{,}000 \times g$ for 15 minutes. The ribosomal particles were sedimented out of the solution by centrifuging at $105{,}000 \times g$ for 4 hours. Like the original preparations of 70S ribosomes, the particles sedimented from NH_4Cl contained 60% RNA and 40% protein; i.e., no appreciable loss of ribosomal protein was noted following treatment with NH_4Cl.

If the sediment consisting of "ribonuclease-free" ribosomal subunits, obtained as above, was suspended in deionized water or even in a 0.01*M* tris buffer free of Mg^{++} (see schematic presentation of the experiment, Fig. 6), a distinct picture of unfolding, or loosening, of the previously compact particles became apparent. This could be attributed largely to changes in the hydrodynamic properties involving a drop of sedimentation coefficients from 45 and 30 to 24-26 and 12-15 Svedberg units, respectively, with a simultaneous considerable increase in viscosity. (These values, obtained experimentally, have not been extrapolated for infinite dilution.)

In order to analyze in greater detail changes affecting the "ribonuclease-free" ribosomes when transferred to solutions of low ionic strength free of Mg^{++}, the 24S and 14S particles dissolved in deionized water were sedimented in the preparative ultracentrifuge at 105,000 × *g* for 12 hours. Chemical analysis of the sediment showed 60% RNA and 40% protein, which is the same ratio as found for the original 70S ribosomes as well as for the 50S and 30S particles. It follows that the lowering of sedimentation coefficients and the increase in specific viscosity of ribosomal particles when transferred to water are attributable directly to the unfolding or loosening of the ribonucleoprotein particles, with no loss of ribosomal protein and none of it being transferred to the solution. The above changes, therefore, are not associated with a partial or complete release of ribosomal RNA or with any other manifestations involving dissociation of the ribonucleoprotein into RNA and protein.

On the other hand, the RNA, when isolated from the sediment and analyzed in the ultracentrifuge, was shown to consist of the same two high molecular components (23S and 17S) that

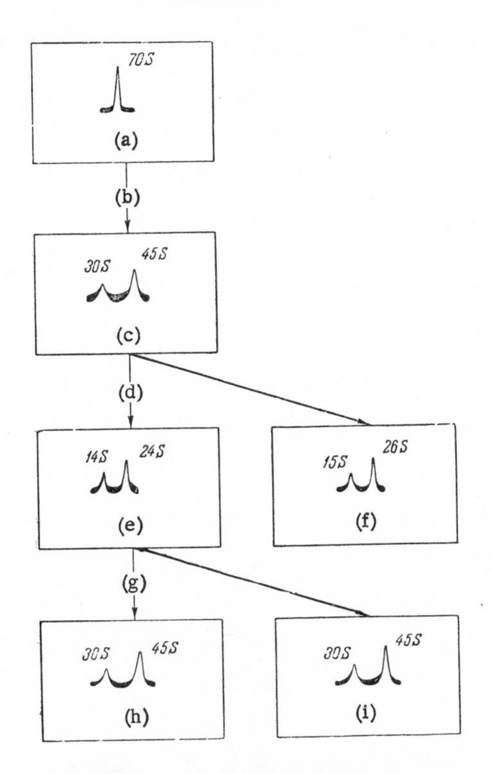

Fig. 6. Schematic presentation of experiment on reversible unfolding of ribosomal particles into ribonucleoprotein strands (the relevant sedimentation diagrams are included). (a) In 0.001*M* tris plus 0.05 *M* Mg^{++} (original preparation); (b) sedimentation at 105,000 × *g*, 90 minutes; (c) in 0.05*M* NH_4Cl (dissociation); (d) sedimentation at 105,000 × *g*, 4 hours; (e) in H_2O (unfolding); (f) in 0.01*M* tris without Mg^{++} (unfolding); (g) sedimentation at 105,000 × *g*, 12 hours; (h) in 0.5*M* NH_4Cl (reversibility); (i) in 0.01*M* tris plus 0.01*M* Mg^{++} (reversibility).

characterize the ribosomal RNA from the native ribosomes of *E. coli.* A rise in specific viscosity was noted for the isolated RNA when heated (from 0.810 at 20°C to 1.950 at 60°C, in a 0.1*M* tris buffer, the RNA concentration approximating 4.5 mg/ml); that is to say, a structure made up of intact continuous polynucleotide chains was established for the acid. Thus, direct evidence has been obtained confirming that the decline of sedimentation coefficients noted for the "ribonuclease-free" ribosome particles when transferred to aqueous solutions does not result from any kind of degradation of these particles to smaller fragments but reflects the unfolding or loosening of each particle as a whole. At the same time, the continuous chain of ribosomal RNA incorporated in the particle remains structurally intact.

The fact that transfer of the ribosomes to aqueous solutions free of Mg^{++} is followed by unfolding of the ribosomal subunits 50S and 30S into ribonucleoprotein strands has been conclusively demonstrated by electron microscopy. Figure 7 shows a typical electron micrograph of a preshadowed preparation containing the 24S and 14S particles, obtained by sedimentation from deionized

Fig. 7. Electron micrograph of preshadowed ribonucleoprotein strands obtained from ribosomal particles. Shadow-to-height ratio 9:1.

water. Alongside the products of destruction, the inevitable handicap in preparing samples for electron microscopy, a large number of strand-like particles can be seen ranging up to 1200-1300Å in length and about 30Å in height (strand diameter), as evaluated from the length of the shadow. Although these ribonucleoprotein strands, as pointed out before, contain 40% protein (as do the normal ribosomes), in external appearance they strongly resemble the "rod-like" conformations of high-polymeric RNA revealed by electron micrographs.

If the sediment consisting of 24S and 14S particles (i.e., "unfolded" ribosomes) was suspended not in water or in dilute buffer free of Mg^{++}, but in 0.5*M* NH_4Cl solution (plus 0.01*M* tris buffer)—i.e., in a solution of high ionic strength—then the sedimentation coefficients of the components rose to their respective values of 45 and 30 Svedberg units. The same thing happened when the sediment was suspended in a dilute tris buffer (0.01*M*) containing Mg^{++} in a 0.01*M* concentration. The apparent indication was that the "unfolded" particles had reverted to their original compact configuration (see schematic presentation in Fig. 6). The unfolding of ribosomal subunits was thus shown to be reversible.

The evidence cited here compels the conclusion that the ribosomal 50S and 30S subunits are particles formed as a result of compact coiling of a long ribonucleoprotein strand, 30-40Å in diameter.

2. NATIVE PRECURSORS OF THE RIBOSOMES

In the presence of chloramphenicol, a specific inhibitor of protein synthesis, the normal ribosomes accumulating in the bacterial cells will be replaced by ribonucleoprotein particles which contain the normal ribosomal RNA and protein, but the latter will be present in considerably smaller quantities than are found in ribosomes. This accounts for the lower sedimentation coefficients recorded for such particles, as compared with the ribosomes. These particles were named "chloromycetin-, or CM-particles" [63, 60]. Other protein synthesis inhibitors cause the appearance of similar ribonucleoprotein particles. In view of this, they can be regarded as incompletely formed ribosomes, i.e., ribosomes not fully packed with protein. "Light" ribonucleoprotein particles, in small numbers, have also been detected in normally growing bacteria [64]. All such particles, therefore, can be identified as the normal precursors of ribosomal subunits ("neosomes"). They accumulate under conditions of inhibited protein synthesis, because the lack of protein prevents them from completing their buildup and becoming normal ribosomes. This interpretation has been confirmed in our recent experiments. It was shown that in the presence of Mg^{++}, the CM-particles combine with additional protein *in vitro*, forming complete particles which are indistinguishable from the normal ribosomal subunits 50S and 30S when tested for all the known indices—sedimentation, electron microscopy, RNA:protein ratio [27] (see below).

It may be reasonably assumed, in this connection, that the CM-particles are not only the metabolic but also the structural precursors of the ribosomes, i.e., they carry within themselves the basic elements of the structural organization peculiar to the ribosomes, perhaps in a "simplified" form. With this in mind, a special electron microscope study of CM-particles was undertaken by the author in collaboration with N. A. Kisselev [23].

The isolated CM-particles in our preparations were found to contain 73-75% ribosomal RNA and 27-25% protein, in full agreement with the literature data [63, 60]. When analyzed in the ultracentrifuge, they showed two peaks, as respective sedimentation coefficients of 25 and 19 Svedberg units (the 25S and 19S particles). The RNA isolated from such preparations consisted

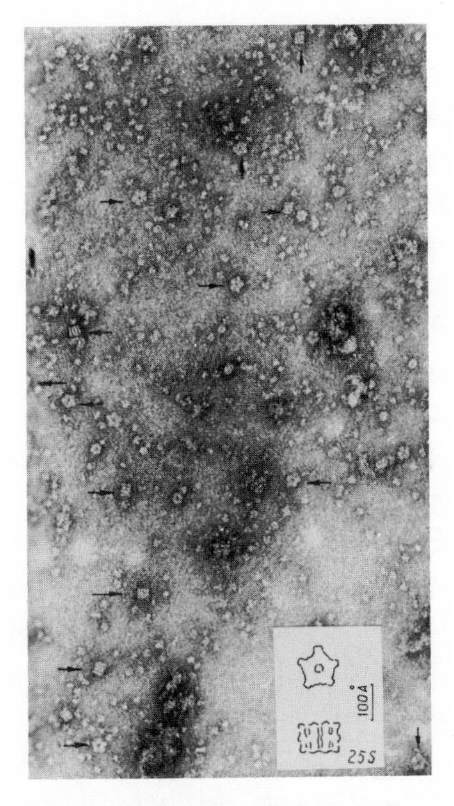

Fig. 8. Electron micrograph of "chloromycetin" ribonucleoprotein particles contrasted with PTA.*

*Phosphotungstic acid.—Tr.

of two components with sedimentation coefficients of 23 and 17 Svedberg units, respectively; i.e., it was identical with the normal ribosomal RNA. An electron microscope study of the CM-particles in a preshadowed preparation revealed two types of formations corresponding apparently to the 25S and 19S particles. In their dimensions, they were very close to the 50S and 30S particles (subunits) which make up the normal ribosome. Some of the particles noted in the electron micrographs of the preshadowed preparation were approximately spherical in shape, ranging 120-150Å in height (as calculated from the length of the shadow). Another type of particles appeared flattened, their height varying between 50 and 80Å.

The structure of CM-particles is revealed in greater detail when the samples are prepared by the method of negative contrasting. A relevant electron micrograph is shown in Fig. 8. A distinction between two types of a regular, ordered particle structure, as revealed in the field of vision, is immediately apparent to the viewer. One type of particle is seen most often in the form of peculiar pentagonal structures, up to 160Å in diameter, with an opening at midpoint. Such a particle seems to be built of five large subunits arranged so as to form a pentagon. The other type of organized formation involves rectangular particles built of four rows of subunits placed side by side, each about 35Å in width. Occasionally, three small subunits can be discerned making up the row. In the particular projection shown, the particles are shaped as rectangles ranging 120-140 × 160Å in size. It should further be mentioned that occasional single strands, about 30Å thick and varying in length, are also noted in the micrographs. The preparation contains a large number of fine particles which are presumably the products of degradation.

As we compare the electron microscope data on the CM-particles with those obtained for the normal ribosomal subunits (Fig. 3b) the first thing that comes to our attention is that in both shape and dimensions, the pentagonal as well as rectangular particles are identical in the two cases. The inference suggests itself that the "pentagonal" CM-particles (apparently, the 25S particles) may be the precursors of the 50S ribosomal subunits, while the "rectangular" CM-particles (probably 19S) may be the precursors of the 30S subunits.

Both types of CM-particles shown in the micrographs (Fig. 8) exhibit a distinct regularity of structure. From this observation, certain conclusions can be drawn regarding the probable arrangement of protein molecules in these particles. We shall speak first of the "rectangular" particles, tentatively defined as the 19S components.* The single RNA molecule that is a constituent of such a particle is known to have a molecular weight of 0.5-0.6 million. At the same time, the RNA accounts for 73-75% by weight of the entire particle, which leaves 27-25% for the protein. Now, the molecular weight of ribosomal protein, according to available literature data [15], equals 17,000-20,000. This means that a 19S particle must contain about 10-13 molecules of protein. In the electron micrographs, on the other hand, 4 rows of small subunits can be discerned in such a particle, each containing 3 subunits, 12 subunits in all, contrasted with PTA. This suggests that each discernible subunit represents an individual

*At a later date, after this material was presented, the initial identification of the rectangular particles as the 19S CM-particles (or 30S ribosomal subunits) was shown to be incorrect. The visible rectangular particles were found to represent another projection of the same pentagonal particles (the 25S CM-particles or the 50S ribosomal subunits). The 25S and 50S particles can thus be described as faceted cylinders 160Å in diameter, 120-140Å tall. This is consistent with the structural analysis of the 50S particle model which will be offered in this lecture. The analysis of the 30S particle model, on the other hand, is incorrect. At the present time the author has obtained more exact data concerning the shape of the 30S particles.—A. S.

protein molecule. We can thus see all the protein molecules (12 of them) which are the constituents of a 19S particle, arranged more or less in one plane, as they appear in electron micrographs. In micrographs of the preshadowed preparation, the 19S particles (as well as the respective 30S subunits) are, in fact, seen as flattened formations. On the other hand, a spherical protein molecule with a molecular weight of 20,000 should have a 36Å diameter, according to theoretical calculations. This is quite consistent with the dimensions of the small subunits discernible in Fig. 8. The 19S particles can thus be described as fairly well-ordered structures which contain 12 protein molecules arranged approximately in one plane, forming 4 adjacent parallel rows, 3 molecules in each. All these molecules must obviously be linked to a single RNA molecule; consequently, the same arrangement of the protein molecules will be found in the single continuous RNA molecule (strand) of the 19S and 30S particles.

Examination of the "pentagonal" particles, which represent the 25S component in the CM-particles, reveals greater structural complexity. It is obvious that the five discernible subunits (Fig. 8) are too large to be identified as individual protein molecules. Particles of this type are by no means flat structures; therefore, what is seen by the observer must be the projection of structural elements arranged at various levels. It is quite difficult, on the basis of such visible pictures, to arrive at any conclusions regarding the arrangement of protein molecules within these particles. More promising, it seems, would be a combined approach to the problem. An attempt should be made to develop a model of the RNA and protein arrangement that would account for the observed picture.

3. RECONSTRUCTION OF RIBOSOMAL PARTICLE *IN VITRO*

The preparations of CM-particles, following the first ultracentrifuge sedimentation from the original cell-free extract, were often found to contain not only the typical 19S and 25S components of the CM-particles but also considerable amounts of a protein component with a low sedimentation coefficient (Fig. 9a). When such protein-containing preparations of CM-particles were suspended in the tris buffer free of magnesium, a second sedimentation in the ultracentrifuge was sufficient to free the CM-particles to an appreciable extent from the accompanying protein. As stated earlier, the purified CM-particles contained 25-27% protein and 75-73% RNA. However, when the preparations of CM-particles were sedimented in the ultracentrifuge for the second time from suspension in the *tris buffer containing magnesium* ($10^{-4} M$ magnesium acetate), the resuspended sediment was found to contain neither the typical 19S and 25S components nor any of the accompanying protein component. It contained, instead, two heavier components, with sedimentation coefficients of about 30S and 50S (Fig. 9b) [27], i.e., exactly those of the normal ribosomal subunits 30S and 50S. Chemical analysis of the newly detected particles gave the relative content of 40% protein and 60% RNA, which is the same as found in the normal ribosomes. An electron microscope study of the preparation carried out by N. A. Kisselev revealed two types of particles, indistinguishable in both dimensions and shape from the 30S and 50S subunits of the normal ribosomes from *E. coli* (Fig. 10).

Thus, simultaneous sedimentation of the 19S and 25S CM-particles, along with the accompanying protein, in the presence

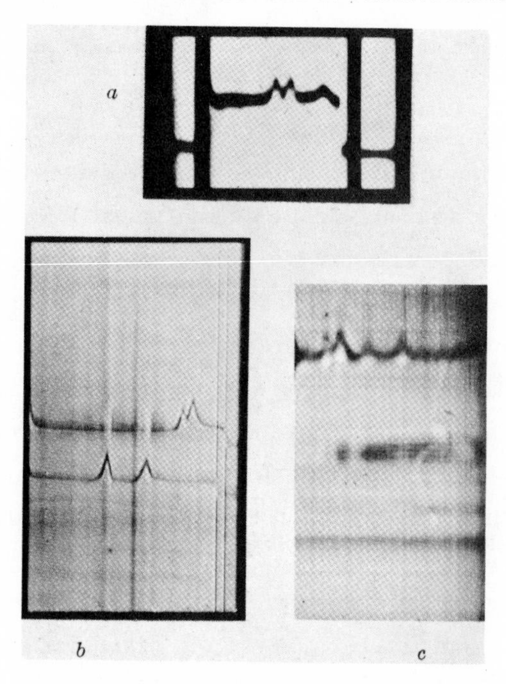

Fig. 9. Sedimentation of the preparation of CM-particles with the accompanying protein in $10^{-3}M$ tris buffer + $10^{-4}M$ magnesium acetate, 42,000 rpm, 20°C. (a) Before sedimentation in the preparative rotor at 100,000 × *g*; 25S and 19S components of CM-particles and slower-moving protein components are seen; (b) lower pattern; (c) after sedimentation in the preparative rotor at 100,000 × *g* and resuspending in the same buffer. In (b) only 50S and 30S components are seen. In (c) four components are visible, the two heaviest ones corresponding to 50S and 30S. [(b) Upper pattern: 23S and 16S components of purified RNA.]

of magnesium ions, carried out in the ultracentrifuge at 100,000 × *g*, leads to the binding of additional protein by the CM-particles. The new particles formed as a result cannot be distinguished from the normal 30S and 50S subunits of the ribosomes when physicochemical criteria are applied for comparison.

The formation of ribosome-like particles from the CM-particles *in vitro* was found to be reproducible only in experiments

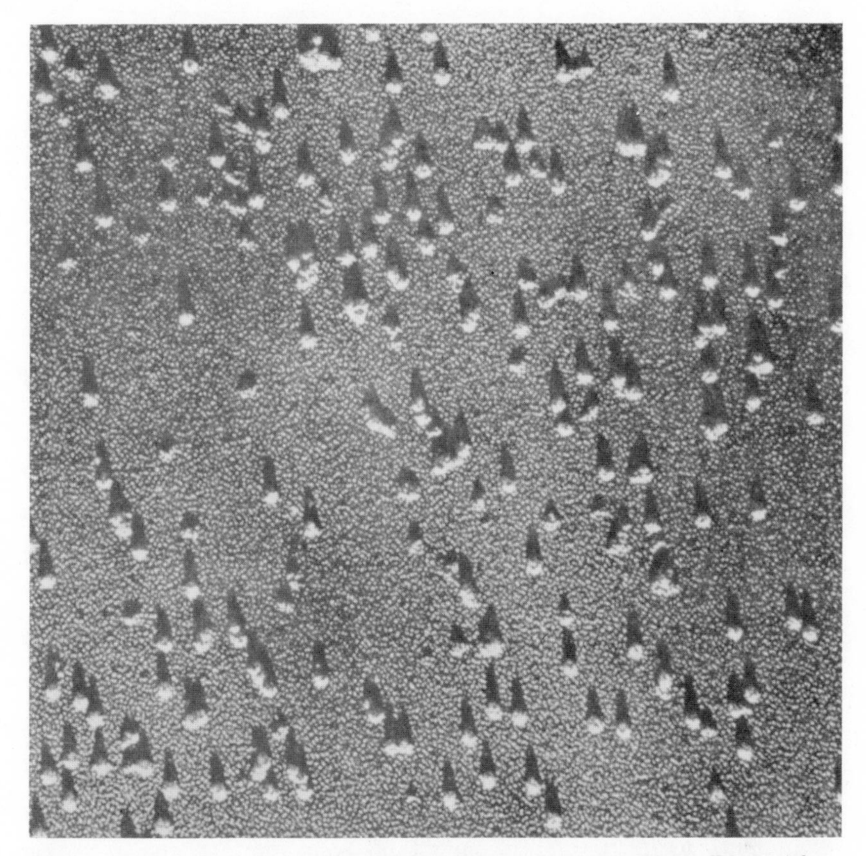

Fig. 10. Electron micrograph of the 30S and 50S particles derived from CM-particles. Shadow-to-height ratio 6:1. Magnification 100,000X. Two kinds of particles are visible; dimensions and appearance correspond to those of 30S and 50S particles in the normal ribosome preparations.

where the original preparation contained the accompanying protein component with a low sedimentation coefficient. Sedimentation of pure 19S and 25S CM-particles in the presence of magnesium at 100,000 × *g* did not in any way affect the nature of the particles. Nor could the reconstruction of ribosome-like particles be attained if the CM-particles together with the accompanying protein were merely incubated in a magnesium-containing solution, without ultracentrifuging. Equally unsuccessful was sedimentation of CM-particles in the ultracentrifuge at 100,000 × *g* in the absence of magnesium.

Several conclusions can be derived from these data. In the first place, the experimentally demonstrated formation of ribosome-like particles from the CM-particles *in vitro* is consistent with the tentative identification of CM-particles as the normal precursors of the ribosomes ("neosomes"), which accumulate in the cell under conditions of inhibited protein synthesis. The cited data, furthermore, may be taken as a possible indication that ribosome formation in the cell may involve a stepwise process and that one of its last stages—the completion of the neosome buildup resulting in a full-valued ribosome—may occur spontaneously in the cell, outside any specialized structure, as a result of a purely physicochemical interaction of the soluble protein with the "neosome." Finally, the above evidence enables us to distinguish at least two classes of proteins in the ribosomes: the *basic structural ribosomal protein*, which constitutes the protein component of the CM-particles and whose linkage to the RNA does not depend on the presence of magnesium ions, and the *auxiliary ribosomal protein*, which cannot be bound unless the neosome structure has been fully developed and the magnesium ions are present. One feels tempted to assume that it is this auxiliary ribosomal protein that is responsible for the enzymic activities exhibited by the ribosomes, while the basic structural protein is the nonenzymic, purely structural constituent of the ribosomal particles.

4. HYPOTHETICAL MODEL OF THE RIBOSOME STRUCTURE

The most important result thus far yielded by our experiments is that the compact ribosomal particles were caused to unfold, reverting to long ribonucleoprotein strands 30-40Å in diameter, with no apparent degradation of either the nuclein or the protein components. This and other available evidence warrant some speculation with regard to the possible structure of such a ribonucleoprotein strand and the way it is packed in the ribosomal particle.

As pointed out before, two unrelated sets of data—those on hypochromic effect in the ribosomal RNA, which is a ribosome constituent, and those of X-ray analysis of the ribosome structure—demonstrate that the ribosomal RNA, as part of the ribosomal particle composition, is characterized by a secondary structure, with some helical areas perhaps of the same nature and structure as found in free RNA in solution. With respect to free high-polymeric RNA, we know that its conformation, which has a secondary structure, consists basically of a large number of relatively short helical areas interconnected with flexible single-stranded sections [40, 44, 16]. According to our data, the axes of these helical areas, under certain conditions, tend to orient themselves in parallel planes. They are "stacked up," forming a strand, or a "rod-shaped" structure, in which the helical areas are oriented at right angles to the long axis of this strand or rod [9, 12, 16] (Fig. 1). The RNA rod was shown to have a diameter of about 30Å, according to electron microscope determinations based on the height of preshadowed particles. This corresponds to the average length of a helical area comprising approximately one full turn of a double helix [10, 11]. The same value of about 30Å, based on electron microscopy, was established in the current study for the diameter of a ribonucleoprotein strand produced by the unfolding of a ribosomal particle (Fig. 7) [23].

From the electron microscope observations reported by Huxley and Zubay [53], who used uranyl acetate to achieve positive contrasting of the RNA component of the ribosome, it follows that protein and RNA remain consistently and uniformly interlaced through the entire mass of the ribosome. What this implies is that the protein molecules must accompany in a fairly uniform manner the coiled RNA structures, such as they are, along their full length. Thus, no outer protein membrane is built around the "coil" of ribosomal RNA (as in the case of the viruses). It is possible that the long, flexible "rod" of ribosomal RNA, as described above, is originally linked along its length with protein molecules (perhaps packed directly between the helical areas), and then becomes coiled or folded in a compact, nearly spherical particle identified as the ribosome. If true, this will account for the apparent uniform interlacing of protein with RNA within the ribosome.

Thus, our data indicate that each ribosomal particle (more exactly, each 50S or 30S subunit) is built from a single ribonucleoprotein strand folded in some definite way. There are reasons to believe that the strand is formed basically by a molecule of ribosomal RNA which has assumed a "rodlike" (strand-shaped) configuration, with helical areas possibly oriented at right angles to the direction of the strand. The molecules of ribosomal protein may be linked with the RNA molecule in such a way that they do not seriously disrupt the RNA conformation as they insinuate themselves between the helical areas and thus "impregnate" the RNA strand.

In attempting to design models representing the spatial arrangement of a ribonucleoprotein strand forming a ribosome, we relied on experimental data yielded by electron microscopy of

CM-particles, since they clearly demonstrate a distinct regularity pattern in the arrangement of the individual structural elements [23]. The similarity in dimension, shape and certain fine details between the CM-particles and the normal ribosome particles makes it possible to interpolate the observed regularities in constructing ribosome models.

The formation of a 30S particle (or of its precursor, the 19S particle) from a ribonucleoprotein strand can be visualized as the result of a triple bend in the strand, with the folds arranged in parallel in one plane. The four parallel sections adhere tightly to one another, due to interaction of the protein molecules incorporated in the strand. The flat rectangular particle formed as a result is characteristic both for the 30S ribosomal subunit and for its precursor, the 19S particle (Fig. 8).* The formation of a 30S subunit from a ribonucleoprotein strand is shown schematically in the left-hand portion of Fig. 11. A photograph of the model is presented in Fig. 12a.

In constructing the model of a 50S particle, we tended to base our structural design on the same basic arrangement as discovered earlier in the study of 19S and 30S particles. The principle involves a uniform bending of the strand at points 120Å apart, with the folds arranged in parallel and adhering closely to one another (apparently, because the molecules of ribosomal protein tend to interact). By extending this principle to the case of a strand measuring 1200Å in length (i.e., the strand of a 50S subunit), we obtained not four folds, as found for the 30S and 19S particles, but 10 folds, or parallel rows, all of which are constituent parts of the same strand. This type of structure,

---

*See footnote on page 181.

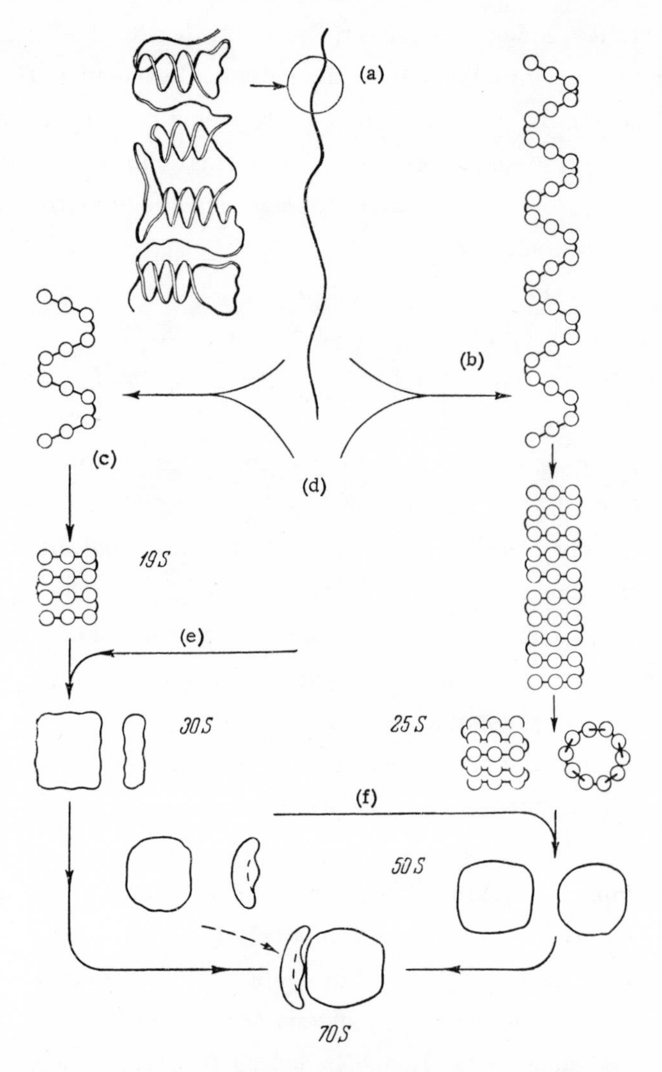

Fig. 11. Schematic presentation of a possible route by which ribosomal particles become organized from a ribonucleoprotein strand. (a) RNA; (b) RNP; (c) RNP; (d) protein; (e) auxiliary protein; (f) auxiliary protein.

comprising 10 parallel rows arranged in one plane and formed by bends in a single continuous strand, can be seen in the schematic presentation shown in the right-hand portion of Fig. 11.

The same principle governing the formation of such a structure by multiple bending of a single strand is demonstrated in the photograph of a mock model of a 50S particle (Fig. 12b). If we now assume that this flat particle will tend to coil into a cylinder, due to interaction of its end rows (this becomes a possibility, considering the length of the particle), we obtain a model of the 25S and, consequently, of the 50S prototype (Fig. 11, right-hand portion). End view of such a cylinder from above (see photo of the model, Fig. 12c) shows each pair of folds standing upright

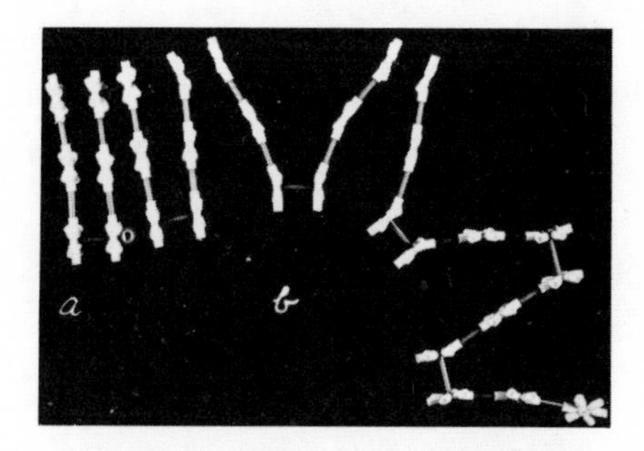

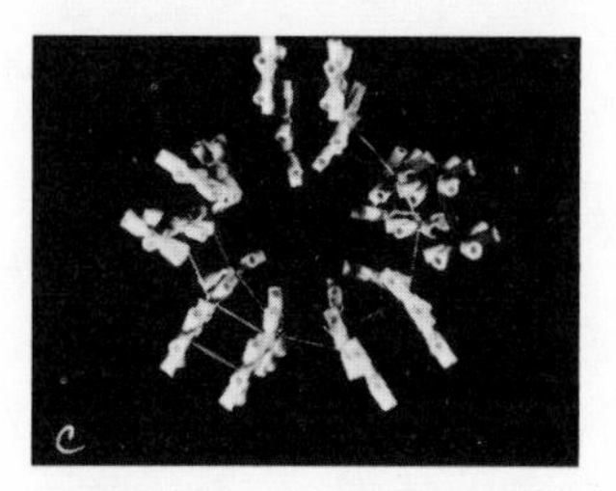

Fig. 12. Photographs representing a schematic model of a folded ribonucleoprotein strand (a, b); also, one variant of the folding arrangement identified as a 50S particle (c).

and joined at the top, so that in this projection they will appear as one large subunit. Altogether, five large subunits will be seen, forming a circle with an opening at the center (Fig. 12c). The view is similar to the one obtained for the 25S CM-particles, which are seen in the electron micrograph as "pentagonal" structures (Fig. 8).

In conclusion it should be stressed that the proposed configurations—"flat rectangle" for the 30S particle and "cylinder," or more correctly a "pentagonal* prism" for the 50S particles—are merely rough approximations describing the basic arrangement of the strand. They do not necessarily reflect the actual shapes of these particles in every detail. More likely, additional bends develop in the folds of the strand as the particle is formed, which render its shape more complex. The 30S particle, for example, is probably not quite flat. Because of further bending of the folds at midpoint, it may resemble a gable roof (see general view of the model, Fig. 13a). The 50S particle, as a result of similar additional bending of each fold in the strand, may easily take on a shape closely resembling a polyhedron or a sphere (see general view of the model, Fig. 13b).

5. A HYPOTHETICAL ROUTE OF RIBOSOME FORMATION IN THE CELL

Ribosome formation in the cell, because of its very nature, cannot be defined as a single-step purely biosynthesizing process. The mere fact that the ribosomes consists of two biopolymers—nucleic acid and protein—synthesized by two independent routes, points to the complexity of ribosome formation. It can scarcely

*The author uses "пятигранник"—pentahedron—i.e., a faceted figure consisting solely of pentagonal faces. The term does not apply here, since the author's "cylinder" has a pentagonal base and top, but the 5 sides are rectangular; i.e., it is a pentagonal prism.—Tr.

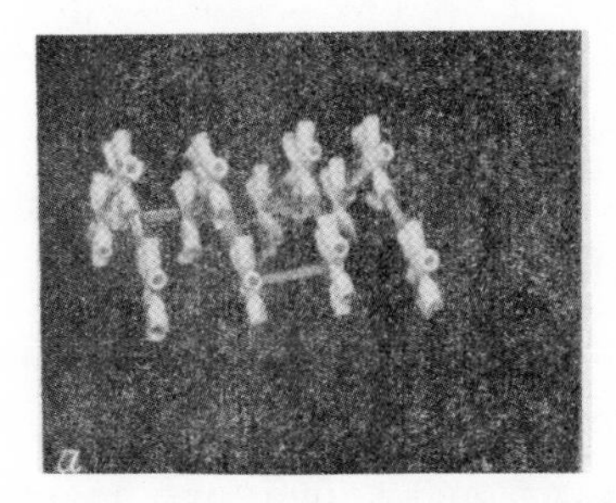

Fig. 13. Photographs showing the final hypothetical models of 30S (a) and 50S (b) particles.

be doubted, in any event, that the formation of a fully developed ribosomal particle in the cell passes through some consecutive intermediary stages. The first stage must involve an independent synthesis of ribosomal RNA (on DNA) and ribosomal protein (possibly in the nuclear ribosomes). The process appears to be spatially isolated in the cell. This stage must be identified purely with the biosynthesis of the ribosomal components. The subsequent stages of ribosome formation should involve unification of the RNA and protein as well as their particular arrangement resulting in some specific structures. It is these "nonbiosynthesizing" stages, reaching a point where the ribosome structure is finally formed from the now available RNA and protein, that will be discussed here at some length.

Two groups of currently available data are most valuable in attempting to establish the actual sequence of events in ribosome formation. One groups relates to the possibility of detecting within the cell some ribonucleoprotein particles, apparently "incomplete" ribosomes, e.g., the precursors of ribosomes, which represent an intermediate stage in ribosome formation. This includes the so-called neosomes [64, 33] as well as the CM-particles which accumulate under conditions of inhibited protein synthesis [63, 60]. Such "incompletely developed" particles contain only half the amount of protein found in the normal ribosomal particles. At the same time, these RNP-particles show no variation either in chemical composition or in their physico-chemical properties, but they represent a clearly defined, discrete group of particles with no gradual transitions or intermediate stages between them and the free ribosomal RNA (or "eosomes") [23] or the fully developed ribosomal particles. This suggests that the formation of ribosomal particles (50S and 30S subunits) from the synthesized RNA and protein molecules is a two-stage process which follows the scheme shown below:

eosome + protein molecules → neosome
neosome + protein molecules → ribosomal subunit

In the presence of chloramphenicol the second stage of this process is blocked and an accumulation of CM-particles sets in. It is characteristic that unlike the fully developed ribosomes, which need the magnesium ions to be stabilized, the preparations of isolated CM-particles are equally stable in the presence and in the absence of Mg^{++}. This may indicate that magnesium ions do not participate either in the binding of protein in the first stage or in the "neosome" formation. The magnesium ions are needed apparently only in the second stage of ribosome formation.

The other group of data, which confirms the above considerations, summarizes our experiments on *in vitro* reconstruction of ribosome-like particles from the CM-particles and protein [27]. In these experimental studies, the second stage in the formation of ribosomal subunits, discussed above, was in fact reproduced artificially outside the cell. The successful attempt confirmed that magnesium ions are needed to implement this second stage. It was further demonstrated by these experiments that the CM-particles most probably can be identified as normal precursors of the ribosomes, representing a normal intermediate stage in their formation. No intermediate states were noted, on the other hand, in the "final buildup" of CM-particles, and with the aid of protein, their structure was that of normal ribosomes. The process appeared to involve a single-step binding of protein following the "all or nothing" principle. In cases where the amount of available protein was insufficient for completing the formation of every kind of CM-particle, experimental reconstruction yielded four types of structures: the fully completed ribosomal subunits 50S and 30S, and the original 25S and 19S CM-particles, with no intermediate formations (see Fig. 9c). All things considered, the successful reconstruction of ribosome-like particles from CM-particles and protein seems to argue forcefully for the assumption that ribosome formation from RNA and protein is not the result of a single-step interaction but a process involving a number of successive stages—at least two—which lead to the development of ribosomal subunits.

If we adopt the proposition that ribosome formation in the cell passes through various stages, it will be of interest to consider anew the feasibility of complete ribosome reconstruction from RNA and protein *in vitro*. Quite a few attempts in this direction have been made at various laboratories, but all of them failed. As we see it today, the failures were unavoidable, since none of the experimenters recognized that the reconstruction must be planned in a series of consecutive stages. We know now that several stages, most likely two, are necessarily involved in this process and that at each stage an appropriate fraction of the ribosomal protein, rather than all of it, must be used up. The difficulty now is in carrying out successfully the first stage, i.e., the linking of free RNA with molecules of the basic structural protein, resulting in the formation of a CM-like particle, the "neosome." In the light of some unpublished observations of Nomura and Levinthal on the metabolism of CM-particles in the cell, it seems plausible that this process, like the second stage, may result from a simple physicochemical interaction of the synthesized RNA molecules with the protein, taking place in the solution. It was found that following addition of chloramphenicol to a bacterial culture, the synthesis of ribosomal RNA continued, while the ribosomal protein was no longer synthesized. This being the case, the structural protein incorporated in the CM-particle was not a newly formed protein. The CM-particles were thus found to be built from newly formed ribosomal RNA and old ribosomal protein synthesized prior to addition of the antibiotic. Moreover, the CM-particles proved unstable in the cell environment, since their RNA became rapidly decomposed, so that free protein, released due to the disintegration of the old CM-particles, together with the molecules of newly synthesized ribosomal RNA, provided the material for the continuous formation of new CM-particles. It would seem, then, that the CM-particles are formed through the bonding of the available RNA molecules with the structural protein of the cell.

In keeping with the above considerations, the formation of ribosomal subunits in a normal cell can be visualized as follows. The ribosomal RNA is synthesized on specified cystrons of the DNA and now emerges in a free state. At the same time, synthesis of the basic structure protein goes on uninterrupted, most likely in some neighboring area, perhaps in the nuclear structures of the cell, so that completed protein molecules are always available in the required concentration. As the ribosomal RNA molecules are synthesized they become linked immediately to the basic structural protein, forming a ribonucleoprotein precursor of the ribosome, i.e., the neosome. In addition to the basic structural protein, an auxiliary ribosomal protein is continually synthesized in the cell, so that its concentration is maintained at a definite level. In consequence, as the neosomes are formed and leave the nuclear structures of the cell they are bound by the auxiliary ribosomal protein through participation of magnesium ions, forming complete ribosomal subunits. Two unequal ribosomal subunits are paired to form a ribosome, with the magnesium ions again participating in the process.

What happens when protein synthesis is inhibited by chloramphenicol, as seen in the light of the same concepts? The synthesis of ribosomal RNA goes on, while the synthesis of both types of ribosomal protein ceases. This does not mean, however, that ribosome formation is brought entirely to an end. It can continue for some time at the expense of stored-up protein still present in the cell. Eventually, the continued synthesis of the ribosomal RNA will lower the concentration of ribosomal protein in the cell to a level at which protein molecules will no longer be bound by the RNA to form new ribosomal particles, i.e., the ribosome formation will come to an end. Inasmuch as two unrelated types of ribosomal proteins are available, their respective threshold concentrations are likely to be different. Actually, chloramphenicol was found to cause an accumulation of neosomes, which are the products of basic structural protein being bound by RNA, while the second stage, i.e., the bonding of auxiliary protein, failed to develop. It follows that the lowest threshold concentration is reached by auxiliary ribosomal protein in the cell much earlier than it is by the basic structural protein. This explains why the second stage of the process cannot go on, while the first stage continues for some time, and the CM-particles further accumulate in the cell until a certain level is reached. Next, because of continued synthesis of ribosomal RNA, the basic structural protein concentration declines likewise to the least threshold value and the CM-particles no longer accumulate. The RNA is, however, not sufficiently protected within the CM-particles from the effect of the outside degrading enzymes (as it is in a complete ribosome). The CM-particles continually disintegrate as a result, and the basic structural protein, released in a free state, is reutilized; i.e., it is bound by newly synthesized RNA, so that more CM-particles are formed. Under these conditions the CM-particle concentration in the cell is maintained at a constant level.

It was demonstrated in our experiments on ribosome reconstruction that the concentration of free ribosomal proteins in the cell is likewise maintained at a certain level and that a definite minimum threshold value exists, below which the protein loses its effectiveness as builder of ribosomal particles. In fact, simple incubation of magnesium ions, as was to be expected, failed to effect any "completed buildup." Such "completion" was achieved, however, when the CM-particles were sedimented together with free protein, so that the protein concentration in the sediment was obviously much higher than in the original extract. It follows that while some protein, in a free state, needed for the "completion buildup" of CM-particles to form the ribosomes, was present in the extract, its concentrations was apparently not sufficient for implementing the second stage of ribosome formation.

6. SOME CONJECTURES CONCERNING THE FUNCTIONAL MECHANISM OF THE RIBOSOMES

Unfortunately, no experimental data are on hand as yet concerning the molecular mechanisms involved in the "work" done by the ribosomes in the course of protein synthesis. The time seems ripe, however, for some effort to be initiated toward gathering such evidence. We thus find ourselves confronting the major problem: What basic premises should be adopted in studying the functional mechanisms of ribosomal structures? From what "angle" should such a study be approached?

At one time the establishment of the template theory of protein synthesis paved the way for a related concept in which the ribosome as well as the template itself, identified with the ribosomal RNA, were assumed to function as some specific surface whereupon amino acids were polymerized to form a polypeptide chain.

It was thought fairly certain that the amino acids, or their complexes with the "soluble" RNA, are all lined up on this surface in a specified linear order, prescribed by the specific sequential arrangement of the template nucleotides, and are next polymerized into a chain.

Subsequent identification of messenger RNA as the true template did not alter the above view. It was still assumed, as the most obvious possibility, that the amino acid complexes with the "soluble" RNA are first lined up on the unfolded chain of messenger RNA and only then does the polymerization of these amino acids take place. The role of the ribosome, in this interpretation, was to provide the surface supporting the unfolded chain of messenger RNA. All facets of the process were supposed to develop in accordance with the laws governing the activity of the common, nonbiogenic catalysts, with messenger RNA and the ribosome functioning in the capacity of a rigid, static surface.

It was not until recently that this viewpoint has to some slight extent been upset as it became evident, under the impact of new experimental data, that the formation of a polypeptide chain in the ribosome is not implemented by a single polymerization of amino acids lined up on the template, but proceeds by way of gradual accretion of the chain, through the bonding of the amino acids, one after another, following rigorously their sequential order. The growth of the chain proceeds in the direction from the N-end to the C-end of the polypeptide [28, 47]. There is no simultaneous lineup of amino acid complexes with the "soluble" RNA on the template. At any given time only a few (1-3) molecules of the "soluble" RNA are present in the ribosome [47, 61]. Today, it would seem, the more recent experimental evidence on protein synthesis could scarcely be reconciled all the way with the conventional concept of the ribosome as a static structure, a stabilized surface supporting the template RNA, which is assumed to be just as static, besides providing the site for biochemical reactions.

I should like, at this point, to expound a quite different concept of the ribosomes as functional biologic particles. The basic, most general premise upon which our hypothesis is predicated is that the ribosome functions not as a static organoid upon whose stabilized surfaces and structural elements various biochemical processes develop but, rather, as a mobile particle easily susceptible to local changes in conformation, which, thanks to these properties, is a "working" particle, participating actively through its interacting components in the dynamic processes under way. The necessary specific local movements of the ribosomal particle as well as the needed changes in its conformation are induced, on the one hand, by interactions with messenger RNA, the "soluble" RNA, with enzymes, the various regulators in the cell, the cofactors, etc.—hence, the exceptional controllability of work performed by the ribosome. It is possible, on the other hand, that each time another peptide bond is formed, a definite sequential order is established in which changes in the ribosome conformation will follow one another. Such a sequence will eventually lead to the next peptide bonding, with the result that a cyclic recurrence of events is ensured throughout the process of polypeptide chain formation. In such a case, the ribosome, during the synthesis of the protein molecule, undergoes periodic changes in its local structures, so that its component parts seem to "stir" now and then.

To what extent is this hypothesis consistent with available data? How good is it in understanding the course of protein synthesis in the ribosome?

Let us begin with the template (messenger) RNA. It is now known that the molecular weight of messenger RNA may be as high as several million [16, 61]. This enormous value, entirely comparable to that established for the ribosomes, corresponds to at least several thousand nucleotides. At the same time, the template function of this RNA requires an unfolded sequence of coding triplets. The length of such a polycystronic template will measure tens of thousands of Ångströms. How can a ribosome 150-200Å in diameter accommodate a template of this size on its surface? A more plausible assumption, it seems, is that this does not happen at all, but that the ribosome, in the course of protein synthesis, is somehow able to "scan" the chain of messenger RNA by running it, section after section, through its own body, so that only one area at a time becomes unfolded as it passes through the ribosome. Thus, the entire code* recorded in the messenger RNA can be "read out" one section after another, triplet after triplet. This is consistent with the idea of successive accretion of the polypeptide chain in the process of buildup.

As regards the "soluble" RNA, it is now known that at any given time in the course of polypeptide synthesis, one or two, at any rate very few, molecules of this acid are present in a single ribosome [47, 61]. This means that there is actually no such thing as a large number of adaptors distributed over the triplets of an unfolded template. Once again, the unfolding of the entire template is seen to be unnecessary. What happens, in effect, is that at any given time a single restricted area of the template becomes unfolded and thus exposed to interaction with the adaptor RNA. The idea that as the template RNA passes through the ribosome its local areas become successively unfolded is shown to be consistent with the above information.

Only one peptide bond at a time, it would seem, can be synthesized in the ribosome. This is as it should be if we consider that the unfolded template area passing through the ribosome at any given time is relatively small, with not more than one or two molecules of the "soluble" RNA present, interacting with the template.

What has been said suggests the existence of a sole "active center" in every ribosome, a single fixed site where a peptide bond can form. It points likewise to a definite single area through

*It is rather remarkable that in 1963, analogous "dynamic" hypotheses regarding the work performed by the ribosomes were proposed independently by J. D. Watson, A. Rich and A. Gierer following the discovery and study of polyribosomes.

which the chain of messenger RNA passes and its local unfolding takes place, as well as a single site where the "soluble" RNA molecule is located.

It was shown that in the process of protein synthesis in the ribosome, only one molecule of the "soluble" RNA, at any given time, becomes linked through a covalent bond with the growing end (C-end) of the polypeptide being formed [47]. The polypeptide synthesis goes on in such a way that each successive complex of amino acid with the "soluble" RNA (wherein the amino acid, as is generally known, is bound to the RNA through its carboxyl group) which is brought into the ribosome becomes linked to the carboxyl of the polypeptide through the amino group of its amino acid, while the "soluble" RNA molecule previously bound to the polypeptide is split off. The new molecule of "soluble" RNA remains bound to the carboxyl of the amino acid it has brought in, i.e., to the end carboxyl of the polypeptides, until the next amino acid arrives along with the "soluble" RNA, etc. If this is so, i.e., if there is only one area in the ribosome where the covalently bound molecule of "soluble" RNA can be located, and only one site for the peptide bond formation, then the growing polypeptide chain must be continually shifting, as though it were "pushed out" step by step from the ribosome. This is another possible case of active "movements" performed by the functioning ribosome. Incidentally, the idea of the polypeptide chain being gradually extruded from the "active center" of the ribosome opens new horizons for our inquiry into the formation of the tertiary protein structure. As the polypeptide chain is formed, its characteristic coiling, in this case, may be determined directly, by the surface of the ribosome as well as other ribosomal and "ribosome-related" factors.

All things considered, it may be reasonably believed that the ribosome not only fixes upon itself, in a specific way, both template and adaptor RNA's, but at the same time, through appropriate induced changes in conformation, it coordinates the shifting of the template RNA chain by one triplet with the installment of a new "soluble" RNA molecule which carries the next amino acid, as well as with the expulsion of the polypeptide chain by a single amino acid residue. For example, interaction between a coding set of the template (triplet) and the corresponding "soluble" RNA molecule, an amino acid carrier, alters the conformation in the given area of the ribosomal particle. As a result of the change, the old molecule of the "soluble" RNA, linked to the C-end of the peptide, is replaced by a new aminoacyl-RNA complex, and the template RNA chain is further shifted by three nucleotides. As another peptide bond is formed, the polypeptide chain may be shifted accordingly, by one amino acid residue. With the forward shifting of the template RNA, on the other hand, a new triplet is substituted for the previous one, in the given area of the ribosome, and this in turn opens the way for the next "soluble" RNA molecule along with the amino acid bound by it. The circle is then repeated once again.

Chapter V

CONCLUSIONS

Matters of structure and function in relation to ribonucleic acids have now been seen to involve a multifaceted problem and one concerned with widely diversified aspects of modern biology. The importance of this problem is evident, above all, from the fact that the RNA's are the basis of protein synthesis, the focal biochemical process taking place in living matter. It may be hoped, therefore, that experimental clarification of the broad principles underlying the *molecular* organization of the RNA's will eventually help us gain some insight into many basic principles of *general biologic* organization.

We have considered some nonexperimental material. A few general concepts and tentative propositions were formulated and discussed. In this connection it should be pointed out merely that such theorizing is by no means intended to foster abstract speculations or mental gymnastics in place of authentic experimental work. These ideas are our *working* hypotheses. They represent a point of view, a platform, upon which our work is based—a point of departure in charting the course of our research and in planning our experiments. When we spoke of our currently adopted line of studies, it was necessary to state our point of view. Our basic approach to the problem of structure in relation to function had to be defined. There would be no point, it seems, in discussing *a priori* whether or not our viewpoint is correct. If it merely stimulates new experiments, or a novel organization of experiments, its claim to existence will be justified. For the time being we shall hold to this viewpoint, and only the future can tell how fruitful or fruitless it will prove in seeking an experimental solution of the problem.

Acknowledgment. In conclusion I should like to thank the Bakh Committee for the opportunity to deliver this Bakh lecture. It has been a great honor to do so.

REFERENCES

1. Belozerskiy, A. N., Nucleoproteins and Nucleic Acids of Plants. Their Biologic Significance, XIV Bakh Lecture, March 17, 1958, Akad. Nauk SSSR, Moscow, 1959.
2. Belozerskiy, A. N. and Spirin, A. S., Nature, 182, 111, 1958.
3. Belozerskiy, A. N. and Spirin, A. S., Izvestiya Akad. Nauk SSSR, Ser. Biol., No. 1, 64, 1960.
4. Belozerskiy, A. N. and Spirin, A. S., The Nucleic Acids (Eds. E. Chargaff and J. N. Davidson), 3, 147, Acad. Press, N. Y., 1960; Nucleic Acids, 123, IL, Moscow, 1962.
5. Bogdanova, Ye. S., Gavrilova, L. P., Dvorkin, G. A., Kiselev, N. A. and Spirin, A. S., Biokhimiya, 27, 387, 1962.
6. Bresler, S. Ye., Kushner, V. P. and Frenkel', S. Ya., Biokhimiya, 24, 685, 1959.
7. Gavrilova, L. P. and Spirin, A. S., Biokhimiya, 24, 503, 1959.
8. Gavrilova, L. P., Spirin, A. S. and Belozerskiy, A. N., Doklady Akad. Nauk SSSR, 126, 1121, 1959.
9. Dvorkin, G. A. and Spirin, A. S., Doklady Akad. Nauk SSSR, 135, 987, 1960.
10. Kiselev, N. A., Gavrilova, L. P. and Spirin, A. S., Doklady Akad. SSSR, 138, 692, 1961.
11. Kiselev, N. A., Gavrilova, L. P. and Spirin, A. S., J. Mol. Biol., 3, 778, 1961.
12. Spirin, A. S., J. Mol. Biol., 2, 436, 1960.
13. Spirin, A. S., Biokhimiya, 26, 511, 1961.
14. Spirin, A. S., International Colloquium on Ribonucleic Acids and Their Polyphosphates, Strasbourg, July 6-12, 1961, CNRS (National Scientific Research Center), Paris.
15. Spirin, A. S., Coll.: Advances in Biological Chemistry, 4, 93, Akad. Nauk SSSR, Moscow, 1962.

16. Spirin, A. S., Progress in Nucleic Acid Research (Eds. J. N. Davidson and W. E. Cohn), 1, 301, Acad. Press, N. Y., 1963.
17. Spirin, A. S., Some Problems Relating to the Macromolecular Structure of Ribonucleic Acids, Akad. Nauk SSSR, Moscow, 1963.
18. Spirin, A. S. and Belozerskiy, A. N., Doklady Akad. Nauk SSSR, 113, 650, 1957.
19. Spirin, A. S., Belozerskiy, A. N., Shugayeva, N. V. and Vanyushin, B. F., Biokhimiya, 22, 744, 1957.
20. Spirin, A. S. and Gavrilova, L. P., Izvestiya Akad. Nauk SSSR, Ser. Biol., No. 4, 504, 1961.
21. Spirin, A. S., Gavrilova, L. P. and Belozerskiy, A. N., Doklady Akad. Nauk SSSR, 125, 658, 1959.
22. Spirin, A. S., Gavrilova, L. P., Bresler, S. Ye. and Mosevitskiy, M. I., Biokhimiya, 24, 938, 1959.
23. Spirin, A. S., Kiselev, N. A., Shakulov, R. S. and Bogdanov, A. A., Biokhimiya, 28, 920, 1963.
24. Spirin, A. S. and Mil'man, L. S., Doklady Akad. Nauk SSSR, 134, 717, 1960.
25. Talmud, D. L., Coll.: Report on Proteins, 18, Akad. Nauk SSSR, Moscow-Leningrad, 1948.
26. Shakulov, R. S., Aytkhozhin, M. A. and Spirin, A. S., Biokhimiya, 27, 744, 1962.
27. Shakulov, R. S., Bogdanov, A. A. and Spirin, A. S., Doklady Akad. Nauk SSSR, 153, 224, 1963.
28. Bishop, J., Leahy, J. and Schweet, R., Proc. Nat. Acad. Sci. USA, 46, 1030, 1960.
29. Boedtker, H., Biochim. et biophys. acta, 32, 519, 1959.
30. Boedtker, H., J. Mol. Biol., 2, 171, 1960.
31. Bonhoeffer, F. and Schachman, H. K., Biochem. Biophys. Res. Commun., 2, 366, 1960.
32. Brenner, S., Jacob, F. and Meselson, M., Nature, 190, 576, 1961.
33. Britten, R. J., McCarthy, B. J. and Roberts, R. B., Biophys. J., 2, 83, 1962.
34. Brown, L. and Zubay, G., J. Mol. Biol., 2, 287, 1960.
35. Changeux, J., Cold Spring Harbor Symp. on Quant. Biol., 26, 313, 1961.
36. Changeux, J., J. Mol. Biol., 4, 220, 1962.
37. Chargaff, E., The Nucelic Acids (Eds. E. Chargaff and J. N. Davidson), 1, 307, Acad. Press, N. Y., 1955.
38. Crick, F. H. C., Structure and Function of Genetic Elements, Brookhaven Symp. in Biol., No. 12, Brookhaven Nat. Lab., Upton, N. Y., 1959.

39. Doty, P., Reviews of Modern Physics, 31, 107, 1959; Coll.: Problems of Contemporary Biophysics, 1, 138, IL, Moscow, 1961.
40. Doty, P., Boedtker, H., Fresco, J. R., Haselkorn, R. and Litt, M., Proc. Nat. Acad. Sci. USA, 45, 482, 1959.
41. Felsenfeld, G., Biochim. et biophys. acta, 29, 133, 1958.
42. Fraenkel-Contrat, H., Singer, B. and Williams, R. C., Biochim. et biophys. acta, 25, 87, 1957.
43. Fresco, J. R. and Alberts, B. M., Proc. Nat. Acad. Sci. USA, 46, 311, 1960.
44. Fresco, J. R., Alberts, B. M. and Doty, P., Nature, 188, 98, 1960.
45. Gerhart, J. C. and Pardee, A. B., J. Biol. Chem., 237, 891, 1962.
46. Gierer, A. and Schramm, G., Nature, 177, 702, 1956.
47. Gilbert, W., J. Mol. Biol., 6, 374, 389, 1963.
48. Gros, F., Hiatt, H. H., Gilbert, W., Kurland, C. G., Risebrough, R. W. and Watson, J. D., Nature, 190, 581, 1961.
49. Hall, B. D. and Doty, P., J. Mol. Biol., 1, 111, 1959.
50. Hall, C. E. and Slayter, H. S., J. Mol. Biol., 1, 329, 1959.
51. Haschemeyer, R., Singer, B. and Fraenkel-Contrat, H., Proc. Nat. Acad. Sci. USA, 45, 313, 1959.
52. Hoagland, M. B., The Nucleic Acids (Eds. E. Chargaff and J. N. Davidson), 3, 349, Academic Press, N. Y., 1960; The Nucleic Acids, p. 219, IL, Moscow, 1962.
53. Huxley, H. E. and Zubay, G., J. Mol. Biol., 2, 10, 1960.
54. Jacob, F. and Monod, J., Symposium of Society for Development and Growth Study, June, 1962.
55. Klug, A., Holmes, K. C. and Finch, J. T., J. Mol. Biol., 3, 87, 1961.
56. Koshland, D. E., Proc. Nat. Acad. Sci. USA, 44, 98, 1958.
57. Koshland, D. E., J. Cell. Comp. Physiol., 54, 245, 1959.
58. Koshland, D. E., Advances in Enzymology, 22, 45, 1960.
59. Koshland, D. E., Horizons in Biochemistry (Eds. M. Kasha and B. Pullman), p. 275, Acad. Press, N.Y.—L., 1962.
60. Kurland, C. G., Nomura, M. and Watson, J. D., J. Mol. Biol., 4, 388, 1962.
61. Lipmann, F., Progress in Nucleic Acid Research (Eds. J. N. Davidson and W. E. Cohn), 1, 135, Acad. Press., N. Y., 1963.
62. Monod, J. and Jacob, F., Cold Spring Harbor Symp. on Quant. Biol., 26, 389, 1961.
63. Nomura, M. and Watson, J. D., J. Mol. Biol., 1, 204, 1959.
64. Roberts, R. B., Ann. N. Y. Acad. Sci., 88, 752, 1960.

65. Schlessinger, D., J. Mol. Biol., 2, 92, 1960.
66. Spencer, M., Fuller, W., Wilkins, M. H. F. and Brown, G. L., Nature, 194, 1014, 1962.
67. Spiegelman, S., Cold Spring Harbor Symp. on Quant. Biol., 26, 75, 1961.
68. Tissieres, A., Bourgeois, S., Gros, F., J. Mol. Biol., 7, 100, 1963.
69. Tomkins, G. M. and Yielding, K. L., Cold Spring Harbor Symp. on Quant. Biol., 26, 331, 1961.
70. Umbarger, H. E., Cold Spring Harbor Symp. on Quant. Biol., 26, 301, 1961.
71. Watson, J. D. and Crick, F. H. C., Nature, 171, 737, 1953.
72. Watson, J. D. and Crick, F. H. C., Nature, 171, 964, 1953.
73. Zubay, G. and Wilkins, M. H. F., J. Mol. Biol., 2, 105, 1960.